STATEMENT CONCERNING PUBLICATIONS OF RUSSELL SAGE FOUNDATION

Russell Sage Foundation was established in 1907 by Mrs. Russell Sage "for the improvement of social and living conditions in the United States of America." While the general responsibility for management of the Foundation is vested in the Board of Trustees, the responsibility for facts, conclusions, and interpretations in its publications rests with the authors and not upon the Foundation, its Trustees, or its staff. Publication under the imprint of the Foundation does not imply agreement by the organization with all opinions or interpretations expressed. It does imply that care has been taken that the work on which a manuscript is based has been thoroughly done.

Remotivating
the
Mental Patient

OTTO von MERING
School of Medicine
University of Pittsburgh

STANLEY H. KING
Graduate School of Public Health
University of Pittsburgh

RUSSELL SAGE FOUNDATION
New York   ~   ~   1957

© 1957
RUSSELL SAGE FOUNDATION
Printed in the United States
of America

*Library of Congress
Catalog Card Number: 57-11575*

WM. F. FELL CO., PRINTERS
PHILADELPHIA, PA.

Contents

3

Charts and Figures

4

Acknowledgments

THIS REPORT is the outcome of the work and thought of many people. They are dedicated to the premise that the effects of long-term mental illness are partly and even wholly reversible.

The survey received its early impetus and continued support from Russell Sage Foundation. For continuous consultation on various phases of the survey itself, the senior author is especially indebted to Dr. Esther Lucile Brown of the Foundation and to Dr. Milton Greenblatt, Dr. Robert W. Hyde, and Dr. Harry C. Solomon of the Massachusetts Mental Health Center, formerly the Boston Psychopathic Hospital.

Grateful acknowledgment is given to all the physicians, nurses, and aides who gave freely of their good will, time, and knowledge in furthering the survey of their institutions.

Special acknowledgment is made to Dr. Freeman P. Adams, Mrs. Lorraine Bagby, R.N., Dr. John J. Blasko, Miss Catherine Bray, R.N., Dr. Henry W. Brosin, Dr. Leonard J. Duhl, Dr. Addison McGuire Duval, Miss Helen Edgar, R.N., Dr. Elmer F. Galioni, Dr. William L. Grover, Dr. Bernard H. Hall, Mrs. Mary F. Hill, R.N., Dr. Jay L. Hoffman, Mrs. Ethel G. Holloman, Dr. Edward J. Humphreys, Sister Juliana, R.N., Dr. Edward A. Kennard, Dr. Louis H. Kohler, Dr. Leon Konchegul, Dr. Maurice E. Linden, Dr. Elmore A. Martin, Dr. Kiyo Morimoto, Dr. Arthur P. Noyes, Dr. Winfred Overholser, Dr. Lucy D. Ozarin, Dr. Thomas G. Peacock, Dr. John T. Reitmann, Dr. John T. Rowell, Dr. Arthur L. Seale, Dr. Lee G. Sewall, Miss Geraldine L. Shaeffer, R.N., Dr. Alexander Simon, Miss Elizabeth Sindlinger, R.N., Mrs. Gwen Tudor Will, R.N., Mrs. Janet Yaley, R.N., and Dr. F. H. Zimmerman, for expert counsel in the course of the survey.

5

The authors are jointly indebted to Dr. Brown and Dr. Leonard S. Cottrell, Jr., of the Foundation, and to Dr. Fred L. Weniger of The Western Psychiatric Institute for basic contributions to the final formulation and format of the study. Special thanks are due to Miss Margaret R. Dunne and Mrs. Mary Jacks for their unstinting efforts in their editorial and secretarial capacities, respectively.

OTTO VON MERING
STANLEY H. KING

Spring, 1957

Preface

Rays of hope are beginning to penetrate the heavy curtain of despair that has long hung over our public hospitals for the mentally ill. For decades these isolated institutions were viewed primarily as places of custody that seemed to swallow up not only increasing numbers of patients, but of staff who could do little more than survive the deadening effects of the mental hospital's way of life.

In recent years converging medical and social developments have begun to stir new interest in the care of psychiatric patients. Perhaps the greatest hope for improvement lies in the very diversity of ideas, plans, experiments that are currently making themselves felt. The growing success of somatic treatments including chemotherapy, increased use of individual and group psychotherapy in the treatment of schizophrenia, developing assumption of responsibility by the nursing profession for the preparation and staffing of psychiatric hospitals with nurses and aides—these are trends that have strengthened the belief that early and intensive treatment of psychosis may not only be possible, but may keep the public hospital from continuing to be a dumping ground for thousands of "chronic cases."

Intensified studies and experimental work going on in psychiatric teaching and research institutes, in special research programs, in pharmaceutical laboratories, and in university departments of social science testify to new zeal in a renewed attack upon the problem of mental illness. The growing realization that greatly enlarged financial provision must be made for the training and remuneration of personnel—not only psychiatric and nursing personnel, but occupational and recreational therapists, social workers, clinical and social psychologists, sociologists, and social

7

anthropologists—is perhaps the most significant indication that change is taking place.

Even the architecture and location of those huge public mental hospitals dotting the breadth of the United States are now being subjected to critical scrutiny, as cognizance is taken of the fact that the form and situation of buildings are determinants of psychological as well as physical aspects of patient care. Possibly much smaller hospitals, planned to incorporate more of the positive aspects of home and community living, so thinking runs, might become therapeutic instrumentalities in themselves. In the location of mental hospitals consideration would be given to proximity not only to professional schools and general hospitals but to sources of recruitment of ancillary personnel, to the population served, and to cities that can provide the hospital with intellectual and recreational stimulation. Probably very different kinds of institutions should be built for those patients needing intensive psychiatric treatment and those, primarily elderly, who have experienced severe cerebral damage.

Thinking that has envisaged potential changes of this order has opened the door to the initiation of many small but encouraging experiments. Day or night hospital units have begun to find a place for themselves as a service to patients who can get along without complete hospitalization. A few "half-way houses" have appeared as bridges between institutional and community living for persons who may go to work during the day, but need the comfort of acquaintances and a homelike environment at night during a difficult transitional period. Outpatient departments, long unknown to most state hospitals, in some places have become flourishing services designed to keep the maximum number of persons from having to be admitted to the institution or to permit discharge sooner. Realization that many patients can take earlier and greater responsibility for themselves and for others than had formerly been assumed possible is finding expression in experiments with patient government, group discussion units, increased foster-home placements, job retraining, and so on. Discussion groups for relatives, tried in a few instances, suggest their usefulness in preparing families to care more successfully for discharged patients.

Such developments begin to make the mental hospital appear potentially very unlike the isolated, locked-door and barred-window kind of place where both patients and staff were shut away from the world. The barriers between the institution and life outside it are slowly becoming more permeable. And as this happens, interest is created in taking a more careful look at what is being accomplished in other countries that might yield helpful guides.

Care of the mentally ill in Denmark, for example, had attracted little attention until recently. Enthusiasm was roused, however, when the national ministry for mental health announced that no new psychiatric hospital was to exceed 400 beds, since "it is being demonstrated that smaller hospitals present less difficult problems of design, security, safety, segregation, classification, administration and maintenance than do larger psychiatric hospitals, initially planned mainly for custodial care."[1]

Already Denmark's "large" hospitals (with a maximum of 800 to 1,000 beds) are being or have been divided and are provided with a complete professional staff for women and another for men patients. New hospitals are being built as rapidly as funds become available in order to replace the larger hospitals with smaller, more functional, and pleasant institutions that permit an active work program with a minimum of "security." The new hospitals, moreover, are to be built in conjunction with, or adjacent to, general hospitals. It is intended that they shall also be more convenient to relatives, cultural advantages, and recruitment of staff.

In addition, "special ward homes" are planned for chronic, mainly senile, patients, who are essentially in need of nursing in a homelike environment. The first of these homes has just been completed in Copenhagen. Its provisions for the care of some 250 persons are, indeed, impressive. The ministry assumes that the

---

[1] Gutterson, Alston G., "Ideas Underlying Danish Hospital Planning," *Mental Hospitals*, April, 1956, p. 21. It should be noted that the Netherlands, Sweden, and Switzerland are moving in directions similar to Denmark.

attractive, uncrowded setting will foster better social adjustment even among mentally confused persons.

But there is another aspect of psychiatric patient care in Denmark that attracts the attention of the American visitor quite as much as the ministry's current planning. Anyone who has had the opportunity to visit the public hospital in Vordinborg, for example, is amazed at the lavishness of the ward staffing, the individualization of care, and the degree to which buildings constructed a century ago have been made to appear warm and friendly, if not functional. This is a hospital where the clinical director and the director of nursing spend two hours together in the morning visiting some 25 wards with a total of 450 to 500 women patients; where they discuss immediately afterward problems relating to the management of individual patients, all of whom they know personally, or broader problems of ward living and staffing; where the director of nursing or her assistant again visits the wards for two hours in the late afternoon.

Why, the observer ponders, are nurses in Denmark far more willing to do psychiatric nursing than in the United States? Why is it that 450 to 500 patients can have more than 200 nurses or nursing students to care for them, when many a mental hospital of 2,000 beds in the United States is thankful to have recruited even 50? Why do kitchen and laundry personnel *like* to take patients for a walk after they have finished the day's work? To what extent are answers to these questions determined by occupational and economic factors in Denmark, and to what extent by a perception of the importance and fruitfulness of the work done in psychiatric hospitals? The casual visitor certainly does not discover the answer. He believes, however, that he sees appreciable recognition of the worth and dignity of the human being, even though mentally ill; a recognition that also characterized the era of Moral Treatment in American mental hospitals. He wonders how such recognition can be reinstated and continuously emphasized as a cardinal principle if our institutions are to recruit personnel sufficient in number, ability, and motivation.

The extensive program of foster-home care of mental patients in Geel, Belgium, had long been known to medical historians and to some psychiatrists in the United States. Here was a town that had had a religious mission since the Middle Ages to care for the disturbed of mind that flocked to it. Since no such motivation existed in this country, physicians reasoned, it could not afford a useful pattern for us. But current reexamination reveals that certain components of its success in keeping 2,500 patients in foster homes may rest not merely on the town's sense of mission or the need of many families to supplement their monthly income, but on realistic provisions applicable to other countries interested in developing similar programs. It is a tenet of faith at Geel that a family can be found on second, third, or even fourth trial, if not the first, in which the particular patient will feel relative comfort and security. This very tenet precludes the hospital from assuming that a patient's initial failure is proof of his inability to live outside institutional walls.

The fact that the town is divided into four districts, each with a physician and two nurses, provides professional and psychological support to families and patients alike. Every family knows that the doctor or nurse will presently be making a regular call on it and the patient, that help can be requested at any time, that an ambulance is at hand to take a badly disturbed patient back to the hospital immediately. Everyone is accustomed to those informal visits when the superintendent of the hospital himself unexpectedly calls, generally at the back door, for a few minutes of pleasant conversation with, and a word of praise for, his neighbors and their charge who is also his charge. Under circumstances such as these, families can feel more confidence in undertaking and persevering in the far from easy task of having mentally sick persons in their home.

Of particular interest to those who are attempting to inform themselves about developments in other countries is a report, *Mental Illness and Psychiatric Care in Israel*, presented recently by Dr. Armand Sunier, chief of the Mental Health Section of the Municipal Medical and Health Center of Amsterdam.[1] The

[1] Copies of this mimeographed report, which was presented to the Ministry of Health of Israel, the World Health Organization, and the American Joint Distribution Committee, may be obtained through the Committee's office at 119 Rue St. Dominique, Paris.

report, designed to assist Israel in long-term planning for the needs of emotionally disturbed persons, emphasizes the importance of a wide variety of psychiatric community resources and the place of the mental hospital within the constellation of such resources. Dr. Sunier's exposition synthesizes a philosophy that is the outgrowth of considerable experience in the Netherlands. It might also be regarded as a synthesis of recent progress in thinking in the United States.

The report had its origins in a request made to the American Joint Distribution Committee by the Ministry of Health of Israel for funds to provide 1,000 additional beds for the mentally ill. The Committee replied that although the request had been received sympathetically, its medical advisers considered the available information insufficient to permit the planning of a comprehensive and coordinated program for hospitals, outpatient and other services. They had emphasized that the requirements of mental hospitals for beds reflected not only the prevalence of mental illness, but also the manner in which such illnesses are dealt with. The advisers continued:

> Thus, effective arrangements for the prompt examination and assessment of individuals with more or less acute episodes of mental illness, the availability of forms of care other than the mental hospital, and a variety of social services and social arrangements to facilitate discharge, supervision and post-hospital adjustment of mentally ill patients—all have a marked influence upon the psychiatric hospital bed requirement. At the same time, it seemed reasonable to assume that the flexible utilization of the array of services would tend to assure to each patient the most appropriate type of care.

The Ministry of Health had based its case for needing many more beds primarily upon the existence of a sizable waiting list of mental patients referred for hospitalization. After a careful study of that waiting list, Dr. Sunier concluded that it could not be considered a valid basis for increasing the national bed capacity. Individual case studies showed that the great apparent pressure for admission to mental hospitals stemmed from the lack of readily available alternative types of care. Need existed, in his opinion, for no more than 150 to 200 additional beds, and even they should be made available in diagnostic and short-term care centers in general hospitals.

He emphasized, however, the immediate necessity for expanding the use of nonhospital facilities. Envisaged was an increase of provision for patients in agricultural working villages and the development of hostels, boarding homes, day-care services, and long-stay annexes to mental hospitals. Envisaged, further, was the enlargement and strengthening of the three government mental hygiene clinics, each of which would be expected to cover a region of the country by motor transport. The staff of these clinics would be expected to undertake prompt examination of patients newly referred for care, and also the psychiatric and social after-care of ambulatory patients. Employment, housing, and other social services would be included in the program of after-care.

Finally, Dr. Sunier pointed to the need for a central coordinating committee charged with long-range planning for the full utilization of facilities and services, and with questions of long-range professional development of psychiatrists, psychiatric nurses, and psychiatric social workers.

Such are the ideas and current practices pertaining to the care of the mentally ill in the United States and other countries that are exerting an influence upon state departments of mental health and planning agencies and upon the informed American public generally. All are agreed that broad change and larger positive accomplishment are possible and imperative. Attention is coming more and more to be directed to two major questions: how can the entire mental institution be converted into a therapeutic center with diverse but coordinated forms of therapy provided by many different groups of staff, and what is the place of the hospital among various kinds of treatment facilities?

Numerous individual institutions, however, are experiencing difficulty in raising their sights to the level of seeking answers to questions of such scope.[1] They are the mental hospitals that Dr. Sunier would probably characterize as "old-fashioned," which are staggering under the problem of vast numbers of "chronic" patients. They are so oppressed by the dead weight of hundreds of continuously more regressed persons, many of whom are senile and physically infirm, that administrators and staff alike fail to see how attention can be focused upon therapeutic goals for more than a fraction of the patients. Over and again they ask, "What *can* be done for these masses of hopeless people?"

It is to their specific question that this book is addressed. Until such a time as early and intensive treatment has sharply checked the tendency toward mental and emotional regression and a determination has been made at least about more suitable care for the elderly and physically infirm, hospitals overburdened by such patients deserve all the help and understanding support that can be given them. Fortunately, the evidence presented here, together with much more now available in literature elsewhere, affirms the belief that even long-hospitalized and senile patients need not be viewed as half so hopeless as many institutions in their discouragement have concluded. Both patient behavior and the conditions under which they live can be transformed by social means to a degree that only concrete evidence makes believable.

How to obtain such evidence became a subject of interest to Russell Sage Foundation in the early nineteen fifties. Experiments in improvement of patient care in large hospitals, initiated under Foundation sponsorship,[2] as well as a few other experiments that had already been reported, suggested the desirability of a systematic search for achievements. Needed were examples of how a variety of mental hospitals in different parts of the United

---

[1] In *Human Problems of a State Mental Hospital* (McGraw-Hill Book Co., New York, 1956), Dr. Ivan Belknap, the author, describes one such hospital that is characteristic of many others. He shows how its isolated, impersonal social environment is not only a hindrance to treatment, but to concerted creative planning for improvement.

[2] Greenblatt, Milton, Richard H. York, and Esther Lucile Brown, *From Custodial to Therapeutic Patient Care in Mental Hospitals*. Russell Sage Foundation, New York, 1955.

States had brought about change through practical methods that could be readily initiated elsewhere. Hence, the Foundation asked Dr. Otto von Mering, an anthropologist, who had already spent two years in interviewing psychotic patients at the Boston Psychopathic Hospital (now the Massachusetts Mental Health Center) to visit mental hospitals across America and report on encouraging developments in patient care. As he and Dr. Stanley H. King, a social psychologist who collaborated in the writing of the book, note in their introductory chapter, visits were primarily confined to large state hospitals, since those institutions have borne the major burden of long-term patients.

Encouraging undertakings were found in much greater number than could be reported in sufficient detail to furnish useful guidelines. Those selected for portrayal are confined to patients who were receiving almost no somatic treatments and no individual or group psychotherapy. Thus, improvement in behavior manifested by these patients could not be attributed to psychiatric intervention as traditionally defined. Before commenting on how improvement had been induced, it should be noted parenthetically that some of the encouraging undertakings had been initiated by ward staffs without the results even being known to the higher administrative echelons of the hospital. Over and again a charge aide or attendant, because of his perceptiveness and his desire to improve the patients' lot, or only perhaps for his own survival in an otherwise intolerable situation, had succeeded in introducing on his ward some of the positive values of family life and social interaction. And so it happens that in the very same institution where the visitor finds what the authors have characterized as the Museum Ward with its custodial care of a very restrictive nature, it is also possible to find the cheerful, pleasant Family Ward where patients appear not appreciably different from a comparable social segment of the outside community.

The success of the undertakings in improved patient care reported in this book rests entirely upon what has been termed "social remotivation"—the considered use of the social and psychological components of ward living, and more extensive or better coordinated utilization of the resources of the hospital as a whole and of the community beyond the hospital walls. Generally present in such undertakings are staff, and sometimes volunteers, who refuse to accept the "Legend of Chronicity," believing that conditions *can* be improved and that patients will reflect the improvement. Motivated by this belief, they exercise much patience, kindly persuasion, and systematic prodding in encouraging patients to maintain better personal appearance, relearn habits of hygiene and social conformity, and move in the direction of greater social competence. Moreover, they show great ingenuity in restructuring relationships between staff and patients, and among the patients. Their goals are intensely practical and rarely extend beyond immediate and sharply defined ends. The results that they frequently produce are of an order that makes the ward unrecognizable to a visitor who has seen it only six months or a year earlier.

All too often, however, staff face the successful conclusion of an undertaking to which they have made considerable emotional commitment with the query, "What can we do now?" The task has been accomplished. It was not initiated or viewed as one step in a sequence of planned efforts to help the patient move to the highest level of social competence of which he is capable. Many ward staffs or those connected with various services can, to be sure, assist patients to take further steps as they themselves become more practiced in patient care and in planning for it.

What is currently needed, therefore, is the development of a philosophy of hospitalwide rehabilitation and a long-term plan for putting that philosophy into operation. Gratifying as many of the attempts at social remotivation have been, they have generally been directed to one level of adjustment and one type of patient. The test of the usefulness of the total social context of hospital life as a factor in treatment will lie in a program that is geared to patients on all levels of adjustment and that changes its emphasis as the individual patient improves. The test, moreover, of the capacity of staff continuously to improve their practice and broaden their perceptiveness will similarly lie in such a program.

The initiation of institutionwide remotivation, as Dr. von Mering and Dr. King note, requires the integration of treatment facilities throughout the hospital. It also requires the close co-operation of medical and nonmedical staff in formulating a tentative plan, testing that plan in practice, changing it as principles evolve and experience deepens, and interpreting and reinterpreting it until the staff of every ward or service can see themselves fitting into a treatment chain. Only then will potential means be at hand to help every patient maximize whatever social skill he possesses.

ESTHER LUCILE BROWN, PH.D.

May 1, 1957

1. Introduction

THE DAILY CARE of great numbers of chronic and aging mental patients, often under adverse conditions of housing and equipment, is a persistent problem for the staffs of large public mental hospitals. Their efforts to provide treatment, not to speak of meeting the demands of ordinary living, often encounter frustration. Buildings are frequently old and overcrowded, qualified personnel are scarce because of low salary scales, operating budgets are inadequate, and the interest of legislative bodies indifferent. Of equal importance is the behavior of the patients, who frequently show a declining ability for acceptable social behavior. Improvement, if it occurs, is slow and tenuous. Thus, the mental hospital personnel must often deal with a philosophy of pessimism regarding any cure for those individuals who have been committed to their care.

The focus of public and professional interest has been increasingly brought to bear on these unique dilemmas, which are of everyday concern to hospital administrators, staff psychiatrists, nurses, and aides. The purpose of this book, however, is not to add to the picture of frustration, but rather to tell of some of the courageous and promising attempts to resolve the situation that are being made in large public mental hospitals in different parts of the country. The presentation of discouraging and frustrating material is not to be an end in itself but only a means of affording a better appreciation of positive endeavors. We hope that this report will give support for more hopeful attitudes toward the mentally ill, and fill at least some of the gaps in our knowledge about the treatment of the chronic mental patient.

The background problem is of some magnitude. There are approximately 750,000 patients in mental hospitals in the United

States, occupying more than one out of every two hospital beds available. Ninety-seven per cent of these patients are cared for in public institutions, such as state, county, city, or Veterans Administration hospitals. Available accommodations cannot keep up with the annual increase of more than 15,000 patients, with the result that there is widespread overcrowding. It has been estimated that 74 per cent of all state mental institutions are seriously overcrowded and that 40 per cent of all available beds are in obsolete, deteriorated, and sometimes condemned buildings.[1]

The average length of stay of a mental patient in a state hospital has been calculated at eight years. Only 40 per cent of the patients admitted to state institutions are discharged within a five-year period. In addition, 27 per cent of all new admissions have senile psychosis or cerebral arteriosclerosis. What these data sum up to is the fact that the status of most patients in large mental hospitals is either chronic or aging, or both.

In spite of these serious obstacles there are some encouraging factors. Many patients who are admitted for the first time can be discharged within a few months if active treatment is available. New types of physical therapy hold promise of enabling more patients to return to the community and of making other patients more amenable to care and treatment in the hospital. In addition, there is increased interest in the social and environmental aspects of patient care, and greater recognition of the importance of the total social context of hospital life as a factor in treatment. Until now, the emphasis on social milieu has been limited in large measure to small, intensive treatment hospitals, but there are a few scattered reports available that describe pioneer efforts to make use of the total human resources of the hospital, both staff and patient, in the care of the chronic state hospital patient.[2]

---

[1] The data here and in the following paragraph have been taken from *What Are the Facts About Mental Illness?* National Mental Health Committee, Washington, 1955. See also Morgan, N. C., and N. A. Johnson, "Failures in Psychiatry: The Chronic Hospital Patient," *American Journal of Psychiatry*, vol. 113, 1957, pp. 824–830.

[2] For example, see the following articles, listed in detail in the Selected Bibliography: Azima and Wittkower, "Gratification of Basic Needs in Treatment of Schizophrenics"; Galioni, Adams, and Tallman, "Intensive Treatment of Back-Ward Patients"; Merry, "An Experiment in a Chronic Psychotic Ward"; Miller,

This book will present further examples of such efforts, placing them against the background of social processes in traditional ward care, and analyzing them for common factors that can be applied to other hospital settings.

The material is drawn from a fourteen-month national survey of 20 state-operated hospitals, 3 Veterans Administration hospitals, 4 joint university and state receiving and teaching institutions, and 3 private sanitariums. The survey was made possible by the interest of Russell Sage Foundation in ward patient care in mental hospitals. In 1951 the Trustees of the Foundation made provision for an extended study of ward patient care that would be carried out in two phases and in two distinctly different ways. The first phase was to be an experimental effort to improve ward patient care in a selected teaching and research institute, a representative state hospital, and a Veterans Administration neuropsychiatric hospital. The second was to be a nationwide survey of encouraging trends in ward patient care.

The first phase has been described in a previous report.[1] Centering around Boston Psychopathic Hospital (now the Massachusetts Mental Health Center) and utilizing two other hospitals in the Boston area, an experimental program of ward management was designed and carried out. The ward management endeavors together with expanded occupational and recreational activities resulted in significant improvement in patient care.

The second phase of the project, the nationwide survey, was initiated by the senior author in the autumn of 1953. In selecting the hospitals to be visited, 20 authorities in the field of mental health were consulted. They were asked to draw up a list of hospitals, keeping in mind two important criteria. First, each

---

D. H., "The Rehabilitation of Chronic Open-Ward Neuropsychiatric Patients"; Miller and Clancy, "An Approach to the Social Rehabilitation of Chronic Psychotic Patients"; Peters and Jenkins, "Improvement of Chronic Schizophrenic Patients with Guided Problem-Solving, Motivated by Hunger"; Stanton and Schwartz, "The Management of a Type of Institutional Participation in Mental Illness"; and Willner, "Preliminary Report of the Introduction of Group Psychotherapy on a Chronic Ward in a Mental Hospital."

[1] Greenblatt, Milton, Richard H. York, and Esther Lucile Brown, *From Custodial to Therapeutic Care in Mental Hospitals*. Russell Sage Foundation, New York, 1956.

hospital was to be representative of the prevailing conditions of patient care in one of four major geographical regions of the United States, the East Coast, Deep South, Midwest, and the West Coast. Second, each hospital was to be one which had been able to devise in some areas of treatment new and promising methods of ward care despite generally adverse conditions. In addition to wide personal experience, the 20 authorities had direct access to the relevant information that is available in the files of the American Psychiatric Association Inspection Board, the National Association for Mental Health, and the Veterans Administration Central Office. Their efforts resulted in a total list of 71 hospitals. From this a second list was made, using those hospitals that had been mentioned by at least three of the authorities. The second list totaled 30 institutions. They ranged in size of patient population from 100 to 11,000, with all of the state hospitals having more than 1,600 patients.

Each hospital was visited in turn by the senior author, who spent from a week to ten days in the smaller institutions and three to five weeks in hospitals having 5,000 to 11,000 patients. Data were gathered by interviews with staff members and observations of ward behavior. Interviews with administrative and clinical directors of various hospital departments focused on a discussion of the problems of large and small hospital management as such, seeking the nature of the total hospital context within which different custodial and promising ward treatment programs take place. Next, interviews were held with physicians, nurses, and aides in their particular ward and treatment areas. On each ward that was visited at least one nurse or aide on each shift was interviewed. In addition, whenever the opportunity presented itself, at least two patients from a given ward were approached and sounded out for their views on ward life and treatment.

Ward visits were begun in the continued treatment area and then extended to at least one, and usually two, of the following types of wards: the so-called untidy wards, the hydrotherapy wards, severely disturbed wards, semi-open wards, open wards, and wards for industrial patients. Wherever possible, pairs of wards in each category were studied, in keeping with the emphasis on the comparative approach and the necessity for a balanced outlook. Toward the end of the visitation period time was spent on two to four wards in the admission and intensive treatment building.

Finally, the administrative staff were again visited in order to clear up any misconceptions and misapprehensions that might have arisen concerning the functioning of the hospital as a whole or some of its parts. It was made clear that the purpose of the study was not to criticize efforts at patient care, nor to survey the quality of care as such in state hospitals as a whole. Emphasis was placed on the usefulness of inquiring into the nature of recurrent ward situations that hospital personnel have to face and are solving in one way or another in large institutions.

The general data-gathering approach was comparable to the standard anthropological technique; that is, the investigator depended on observation of activity, use of informants, and direct interviews with persons, usually aides and nurses, who were important to an understanding of ward conditions. He asked what went on, watched what went on, came back to the same ward situation at different times during the day and night, and listened to staff and patients tell about their problems and ways of dealing with different situations.[1]

In the observation of ward behavior, certain factors, or frames of reference, were utilized in organizing the material. One of these was based on the Social Activity Index of Kandler and Hyde,[2] where patients are classified into inactive, active but not "socializing," and active and "socializing." In addition to this, the *ward geography* was kept in mind, the placement of chairs, tables, and other equipment in relation to the door, pantry, walls, and windows. The association between social activity and ward geography was carefully noted, a factor that will assume some importance in the description of certain ward situations

[1] Banks, E. P., "Methodological Problems in the Study of Psychiatric Wards," *Social Forces*, vol. 34, 1956, pp. 277–280.

[2] Kandler, Harriet M., and Robert W. Hyde, "Socialization Activity Index for a Mental Hospital," *Nursing World*, vol. 125, 1951, pp. 343–345. See also Morimoto, Francoise R., "A Technique for Measuring Interactions of Patients and Personnel in Mental Hospitals," *Nursing Research*, vol. 4, 1955, pp. 74–78.

later on in this book. The observer also was sensitive to the various kinds of roles that were being filled by the patients, such as "wall standers," "cigarette bummers," and "the oracle." Again this will take on more meaning in the presentation of material later on.

The observer was also concerned with another aspect of the problem, the value that certain social organizations, such as the organization of a particular ward, have for patients and staff. What purposes do these social structures serve, what benefits do they bestow, what is their effect on the management of ill people? Such questions were constantly being raised in the observer's mind and constituted another frame of reference which he brought to his observations.

In brief, the preceding paragraphs describe the way in which the second phase of the Russell Sage Foundation project of ward patient care in mental hospitals was conceived and carried out. We turn now to the plan of the material to follow. At the outset it was stated that we were concerned with the presentation of encouraging efforts at ward patient care in large state hospitals where limiting conditions are daily realities. Not wishing to add unduly to the familiar picture of frustrations and discouragement in such institutions, a word of explanation is in order about the next chapter. Here we present a description of a social classification of patients and the Legend of Chronicity, factors which we feel inadvertently contribute to lack of progress toward recovery for many patients. Then we describe three different types of wards, called the Museum, Moving, and Family Wards, which may be seen in one form or another in almost any large mental hospital.

The Legend of Chronicity and traditional ward types are reality factors that must be presented as a background against which the promising efforts at remotivation may be seen in sharper perspective. Readers who are associated with the care of chronic mental patients will find much here that is all too familiar. We hope that in the succeeding chapters they will find material that also has a ring of authenticity as well as possible application to their particular situations. Chapters 3 through 8 present a number of case histories of actual situations where remotivation has been put into practice. We have selected cases that illustrate the process of social remotivation on many different kinds of wards and with rather different techniques. The cases come from many different hospitals across the country. Finally, Chapter 9 will present the philosophy behind social remotivation, and discuss ways in which the material from the case histories can be generalized to other hospital situations.

We have adopted certain conventions relative to the presentation of our material which the reader should keep in mind in succeeding chapters. In describing ward situations the term "observer" will often be used. By this we specifically mean the senior author, who did indeed fulfill that role. Whenever we refer to "the Survey" or "the Survey visit," we have in mind the Russell Sage Foundation Survey. Throughout the descriptions of remotivation programs and in the final discussion chapter we have used the word "aide" to designate the group of workers variously called "attendants," "aides," and "psychiatric technicians." To us, aide connotes more clearly than attendant or technician the personal, helping function of staff members that is essential to social remotivation. Finally, the names of hospitals and of people have been changed. In addition to the specific case histories included, there were many others that were equally exciting and encouraging and which contributed to the writing of this book. Also, there were numerous physicians, nurses, and aides who were doing a superb job of remotivating patients, yet who could not be mentioned because of space limitations. Therefore, it seemed that the fairest way to give credit to the efforts of so many workers would be to use fictitious names for places and people.

The reader will note that much is left unsaid concerning the care of mental patients. The purely physical and medical aspects are not discussed unless they bear on the planning for total ward care and treatment. Our main focus is on the social milieu, on the possibilities that exist within the social situation for an improved understanding of the patient and new outlooks for his rehabilitation. We do not wish to imply that the physical and medical aspects of care are not vitally important, including the development and proper use of the tranquilizing drugs. Rather, we would hope to add another dimension to the situation so that the traditional procedures of care and treatment in mental hospitals may be more effectively utilized. Our aim is also to bring staff members of mental hospitals to a greater awareness of what they can do together with the patient in releasing his latent forces toward health. This hope would be fulfilled if they become better able to judge and utilize the patient's innate capacities and skills in terms of what is possible rather than in terms of the here and now of traditional ward life. Thus, they may not only see the problems that confront them in a different light but may also find the courage and willingness to adapt to their own hospitals features of the situations presented here.

2. Social Milieu and Patient Care

We BEGAN the first chapter by pointing out some of the frustrating factors that often make the daily care of mental patients a difficult problem. Many of them are common knowledge to professional people who are specifically interested in the care of persons with mental disease. In recent years many of the factors have become common knowledge also for large numbers of the general public. Today, the man in the street is more likely to be aware of overcrowding, inadequate budgets, and shortage of trained personnel in state mental hospitals than he was twenty or even ten years ago. There are other variables, however, which also contribute to lack of progress in patient improvement and which may not be recognized as such even by professional people. These cannot always be measured or enumerated as clearly as numbers on a budget sheet, or demonstrated as sharply as overage plumbing in a building. Nevertheless, they deserve emphasis and to this effort we address ourselves in this chapter.

Keeping in mind our focus on the social milieu of the mental hospital ward, the first important variable is a social classification of patients, in this case constructed by the anthropologist from his observations of staff and patients and learning how they often spoke of various patients.

A SOCIAL CLASSIFICATION OF PATIENTS

The sophisticated visitor at most large state mental hospitals gets many impressions as he observes ward life, talks to nurses and aides, and watches the behavior of patients as they go through

27

the day's routine. If he has had little experience with mental hospitals but has some knowledge of abnormal psychology, he will undoubtedly think of the patients in terms of diagnostic types: the paranoid schizophrenic with his delusions of grandeur and accompanying gestures that give a picture of the fantasy within which he lives; the catatonic schizophrenic, withdrawn, immobile, apparently beyond the reach of present reality; the brain-damaged oldster with a history of syphilis who forgets where his bed is, or confuses the aide with the doctor, and must be helped like a child; and the manic depressive who is bowed by his guilt and must be constantly watched lest he attempt to do away with himself. He may easily recognize many other conditions which fit a scheme of diagnostic classification and imply information about previous history, or etiology, or the possibility of return to ordinary social living in the community. This is the principal way in which our visitor would classify patients. However, this is not necessarily the only way in which the aides and nurses, or even the psychiatrists at times, classify those committed to their care. The oddities of behavior that an individual patient manifests, the ease or difficulty of handling him, and his ways of helping or hindering the established ward routines are major items of interest to the ward staff and constitute identifying characteristics by which patients are typed.

"Drips and Drags" and Others

The patient population is, indeed, a fertile field for assessments in terms of social characteristics. As one nurse put it: "There are on every ward the doers, the watchers of the doers, and watchers of the watchers." Invariably, individual patients in this threefold social classification receive further descriptive attention. On the more active treatment wards the visitor is told who is the Card Player and Puzzler, the Sleeper or Organizer, the Doctor Chaser, and the Shock Patient. On the more disturbed wards the visitor is shown the Fringer, who unravels his own clothing, or the patient who is called the Collector. Such a person seems to occupy his day by picking up fuzz, scraps of paper, and string in the day

halls and dormitory. The visitor is also shown the Sitters and
Onlookers whose eyes move with the Helpers, Runners, and
Pacers. He also finds that there are many Talkers and Grunters
who expostulate with imaginary enemies and glare at their ward
mates.

Going farther, the visitor finds that many, or indeed most, of
the patients occupy more comprehensive social roles in the eyes
of the staff. For example, there is the Little Patient or the Wee
One, a patient of any age, though often young, who because of
physical appearance and behavior arouses the sympathy of both
staff and patients. He is looked after and treated with paternal-
istic indulgence. The visitor will see the Clown, whose bizarre
behavior may be the object of wisecracks, and whose response is
ingratiating, self-deprecatory amusement which invites further
kidding. Then there is Sneaky Pete, the patient who commits
physical violence, whose role is based mainly on reputation
rather than continuous assaultive behavior. The Pest annoys both
staff and patients with persistent and often irrelevant requests
and conversation. The Lookout, one of the few structural roles
recognized by the staff, sits near the dayroom door and keeps
track of the movements of staff members, missing very little of
what goes on. The visitor will soon learn to identify the Drag,
who is judged by others to do less work than his mental or physical condition would permit, the reverse of the Good Worker. He
will also find that on many wards there is the Ward Boss, who
issues orders to other patients, enforcing them if necessary with
threats of violence. Aides may tolerate him because of his usefulness but be afraid of him because of his power.

These are but a few of the categories for a social classification
of individual patients. In addition, similar social classification is
applied to whole wards, buildings, and even groups of buildings.
For example, there are units for tidy and quiet patients, for untidy and noisy patients, for those who act out or are homicidal.
There are other wards for wheel-chair and bedfast patients, for
those who "have fits and fall," for the "disturbed hydro" and
lobotomy patients, and for the "drips and drags." The staff may
speak of the fact that their "most hopeless" patients live in

"Siberia" or that those who are "badly deteriorated" live in the "limbo" building. Sections of the hospital are often known as the "back wards" and staff members talk about their custodial patients.

Such a social assessment and classification of the patient is a natural development in most large mental hospitals. In part, this is the result of the need and striving for order that takes place whenever a large body of people have to live and work together for a long period. In part, it is attributable to the need for utilizing the patient for ward housekeeping duties and for keeping an eye on his actions with limited supervisory personnel. The staff have to depend on the patient to help with the daily routine. Therefore, aspects of the patient's behavior that bear on the management of patients or housekeeping necessities assume real importance. The nature of the patient's difficulties, of what he can and cannot do, is often stated in terms of how much work he is capable of or how much he facilitates or hinders the management of other patients on the ward.

There are some clear implications of this social classification of patients as far as treatment is concerned. For example, it is easy for the patient's work capacity as such rather than the therapeutic value of work and need for play to become all important. With the necessity for emphasis on efficient operation and patient management, the awareness of treatment principles and practice can grow dim. In fact, when the patient's illness is measured wholly in terms of degrees of social deficit or conformity to standards of ward conduct, the concept of "patient" can be lost. The basic problem of knowing how the patient became ill, in order to know how he can get well, can be changed to knowing only what the patient is like now and how useful he can be to make both ward work and living with him as easy as possible.

The emphasis on social classification of patients rather than specific diagnostic and treatment classification has several basic constituents. First, there is relative absence in most mental hospitals of medical or psychiatric activity specifically designed for the treatment of long-term or chronic patients. Even the tranquilizing drugs have proved inadequate to produce major or lasting changes by their use alone. The second factor is the difficulty that all people have in applying the social definition of the sick role[1] to mental patients in general, and in particular to the chronic cases. In contrast to the patient with a physical disease, the mental patient often does not realize that he is sick, a state of mind that becomes more prevalent the longer he is hospitalized. Furthermore, the mental patient often does not know what part he is expected to play in the process of getting well and may find it difficult to cooperate with the physician or nurse. Also, it is often difficult for the physician to tell the patient in simple language what he should do.

Efforts at the remotivation of chronic mental patients toward a more realistic social adjustment must first face the social classification of patients on wards as a reality factor. It is easy for such a classification to become rigid, thus precluding the tentative and exploring attitude toward the treatment of the long-term and severely disturbed patients which is so necessary to any program that seeks to release the latent social and creative forces in the individual.

THE LEGEND OF CHRONICITY

If a sophisticated observer visits many hospitals and is willing to spend the time in getting to know the psychiatrists, nurses, and aides, he goes away with the impression that a distinct attitude tends to pervade the thoughts and actions of the staff relative to their charges. This we have chosen to call the Legend of Chronicity,[2] and it is the second important variable which contributes to lack of progress in patient improvement.

The Legend of Chronicity has without question grown out of a multitude of situational factors that are fairly typical of the larger public mental institutions in the United States, and have been for many years past. Not the least of these factors is the large

---

[1] For a description of the social definition of the sick role the reader is referred to Parsons, Talcott, *The Social System*. The Free Press, Glencoe, Ill., 1951. See especially Chapter X, Social Structure and Dynamic Process: The Case of Modern Medical Practice.

[2] See also von Mering, Otto, "Legend and Mores of Patient Care," *Danville Hospital Mental Health Bulletin*, vol. 33, no. 3, 1956, pp. 1–15.

number of long-term patients for which there are insufficient skilled personnel and inadequate facilities for giving patients an existence conducive to a reawakening of interest in the outside world. There is also the disease process itself, which becomes more intractable with longer duration, intractable in the sense that it is less amenable to standard medical and psychological treatment. Thus, it is a combination of having insufficient or improper tools on the one hand, and on the other dealing with a process that is most resistive to therapeutic approaches, something that occurs with much less frequency in physical medicine, that accounts for the widespread acceptance of the Legend of Chronicity as an explanation of why "things are the way they are."

The primary manifestation of the Legend is that the words "acute" and "chronic" come to be differentiated more sharply in terms of the consequences in therapeutic action than is generally the case in physical medicine. As a rule, when a mental patient is designated as having an acute illness he is regarded as belonging to a still treatable classification, irrespective of the specific diagnosis, and is therefore a worthwhile prospect for an individualized treatment plan. When the mental patient is designated as having a chronic illness, he is regarded by and large as belonging to an untreatable classification, irrespective of the specific diagnosis and is therefore not a good candidate for the individual therapeutic approach. The designation "chronic" usually does not carry such consequences for therapeutic action in physical illness. For example, even in the case of incurable cancer, one therapeutic measure after another is tried, often to heroic proportions, in the hope that some benefit might accrue and the patient's life be prolonged. The individualized, clinical approach is more likely to be continued with the chronic patient who is physically ill, while with the chronic patient in a mental hospital it is easier to give up this approach because of the feeling that a priori it is a hopeless proposition.

In large mental hospitals the shift from a judgment of acute to a judgment of chronic is accompanied by a subtle and covert change in the expectations of staff relative to the patient's future.

The change in expectation is largely unspoken, for it means an admission of failure, an admission which is difficult to accept for anyone connected with medicine. However, implicit acceptance of a change in expectations can be noted in the statements of staff about individual patients when they express the hopelessness of any active treatment, for they know the patient will not get well.[1]

A secondary manifestation of the Legend of Chronicity occurs in the perception of patients. The majority of long-term patients easily become clinically unknown entities, from which it is just a step to unknown entities in terms of persons or personalities. Remarks of staff members that some patients are "things that are not quite human, not quite living," indicate the distance traveled toward the unknown. Another example of change in perception is evident in the idea that patients do not suffer, exemplified in the statement of a nurse: "He's so regressed that he simply doesn't care any more." A different nurse phrased it this way: "He's reached a primitive form of adaptation, a kind of simple equilibrium." And one who was more sophisticated in the use of language indicated that "any apparent observed change of behavior is merely a case of pseudo-reversibility of chronic behavior." The implication of the changed perception of the patient is that he is a person who is outside society, someone in the process of social dying, a social reject.

One may justly view the Legend of Chronicity as a type of defense mechanism adopted by the staff who are charged with the care of the long-term mental patient. As a defense mechanism it serves to reduce the sense of frustration that the staff can scarcely avoid feeling when they consider their helplessness as far as active and effective treatment is concerned. It defends the staff against the personal responsibility for continued failure to help many patients, and thereby reduces guilt. Rather than reacting to frustration with fight or redoubled efforts, those who accept the Legend of Chronicity respond with flight or inaction.

The unfortunate by-product of the Legend is that it has contributed to the increase in the numbers of long-term patients, for

[1] The subtle change in expectations is not limited to large mental hospitals, as witnessed by the statement frequently heard in smaller institutions, "This patient has received the maximum benefit possible here."

it supports staff inaction and the acceptance of an equilibrium in patient care, allowing patients to withdraw more completely and securely into worlds of their own.

The Legend of Chronicity and a social classification of patients tend to sustain each other. The natural inclination to be interested in the minute-by-minute actions of patients as they affect the tasks that a charge aide or nurse must get done on a ward is enhanced by the implicit feeling that the chronic patient cannot get well and that one must devise acceptable ways of dealing with him day after day. That these ways of dealing with him center around the demands of ward maintenance and administration rather than the needs of the patient should now come as no surprise. What begins as an interest in human interaction can easily become rigidified in a pattern designed for the day-to-day occurrences of an interminable stay.

PATTERNS OF PATIENT CARE

The problem of patient care has been met in a number of ways in practically all large mental hospitals. In the course of the Russell Sage Foundation Survey the observer was struck not only by the factors that lie behind the care of long-term patients, that is, social classification and the Legend of Chronicity, but also by the patterns of care that have developed. Although there were variations within and between hospitals, there seemed to be three main types, which we have called the Museum Ward, the Moving Ward, and the Family Ward. In the following sections we present a composite sketch of each type, drawn from the observations of many wards, but representing the "ideal type" from which variations can be seen in any large mental hospital. Each tries in its own way to meet the problems of the daily care of the mental patient in the hospital.

Museum Ward

Starting a careful examination of patient life on some representative wards, the visitor is told that he will have to wait a few minutes until an escort attendant is available before a visit can be made to Ward A. The guide explains that the patients are unpredictable and that it is not wise to take chances. When at length the attendant arrives, the door is unlocked, and the visiting party enters the ward, the visitor may wonder why so many precautions were necessary. The ward is relatively quiet, with most of the patients in regulation overalls and scuffies, sitting on benches or chairs, or on the floor in the dayroom. A few are pacing the hall with measured tread, but their heads are down and they seem to take no notice of the strangers. In one corner of the dayroom there is some activity. A number of patients can be seen walking around, gesticulating, remonstrating with imaginary companions. The area in which their activity takes place appears to be bounded by a few heavy benches set out from the wall as a kind of fence. A sense of subdued orderliness pervades the scene, but there is no welcoming sign from the inhabitants.

The visitor is escorted to the charge attendant's desk, which he notices is located so that the attendant with a quick glance can survey the dayroom and connecting hall. Seated at his desk, reading a magazine, the attendant periodically views the scene in front of him, then returns to his reading.

The visitor pauses at the desk to look at the ward from this vantage point. He notes that the patients are seated in a rough kind of order, those closest to the desk in rocking chairs, the next row in straight chairs, the last row on benches. Beyond, a few patients are sitting on the floor against the wall, or lie sprawled in a corner. They seem to be asleep, although their eyes are open. At one side of the rows a few patients sit around a table as if they were deliberating in a conference, yet on closer inspection each acts as though he were there alone. This is ward geography, the observer realizes, a definite arrangement of the ward furniture and patients according to a preconceived pattern.

He turns next to the human element, the faces of those arrayed in front of him. They seem passive and withdrawn, hardly aware of his presence. However, a closer look suggests that the visitor's every move is under scrutiny. A vigilant gaze is turned on the ward scene while patients permit flies to crawl on their noses without twitching a muscle. Although retracted into their own private worlds the intrusion is noted, noted and combined with an apparent indication of resentment or even hostility. The blank stare does not seem quite so blank as it did at first.

The visitor's attention moves back to the physical characteristics of the ward again. The furniture is durable, mostly heavy oak, but hard and uncomfortable looking. There seem to be no personalized comforts, such as rugs, or draperies at the windows; no pictures on the walls, or mirrors, nothing to break the monotony of drab, brown walls, dark furniture, and screened windows. The ward is clean though, the floors polished, and the smell of pine oil strong in the nostrils; drab and uncomfortable but clean.

Knowing the staff's inclination to type patients according to social characteristics and the roles they play, the observer is eager to know what types there are on this ward. He can pick out several readily. The Sitters, Standers, and Squatters are obvious. So are the Pacers and the Hallucinators. He soon learns that there are also Mutterers, patients who talk to themselves or to the air, often inaudibly, and usually without making much sense. There are Oracles or High Priests, patients whose behavior is marked by obvious mannerisms or ritualistic acts, which set them off from the other patients. For example, he sees one patient at the back of the dayroom, shuffling bits of paper back and forth between his hands and making a repetitive noise which becomes louder in cycles. The attendant tells him that there are a few Fringers, those who unravel their clothes thread by thread. There are also many Sneaky Petes, hence the need for the escort attendant when he came to visit. The patients who sit around the table off to the side from the rows of chairs and benches are known as the Board of Directors.

Although the classification categories are quite numerous, there are many that seem to be missing. There are no Clowns, no Gripers, no Readers, no Traders (indeed, there is little if anything that they could use for their wares). There are no Loverboys, patients who are reported to have attempted to relate to a female patient or staff member in a sexual manner. There may be an occasional Cigarette Bummer, but there are no Teasers. The patient who deliberately annoys other patients cannot live here.

The classification is mainly in terms of physical activity or mannerisms, hardly ever in terms of interaction or definite social roles. The visitor notes this especially when he finds out that there are Patient Workers on this ward but he does not hear anything about Patient Helpers.

Having seen what the ward looks like and obtained a picture of the kinds of people there, the next question concerns the way the ward is run and what the goals of the staff seem to be. Information here may throw some light on the kinds of patients there are and help to explain their withdrawn yet watchful behavior.

Not many visits to this ward are required to find out that things are run by a system, that there are clear rules of behavior, and that enforcement is strict and swift. Definite times during the day are set aside for washing, eating, sitting, sleeping, and eliminating. Patients are lined up for meals, showers, or toilet, and pushed or pulled through the routine. Every day the same people are helped in the same way, or led by the same patients, to these various functions, so that behavior takes on a routine and sameness too. The same patients sit on the same chair or lie in the same corner all the time. Like a flight engineer checking his bank of dials and gauges, the attendant can know at a glance if something is out of place or not quite right. One might say he has more of a positional awareness of his charges than a personal awareness. Variation from this pattern comes only with permission, like the child in school who must raise his hand for permission to go to the toilet. If too many patients start talking or moving around excessively, they are forced to be quiet or sit down, for otherwise the charge attendant feels he would not be able to do his job. Even the chair arrangement fits into this pattern, the chairs and benches being directed toward the attendant so that he can survey the situation at a glance. Agitated patients are tied down, or put in seclusion rooms, sent to hydrotherapy, or put in wet packs. The latter not only quiet them but leave them enervated for some time, which is to say, a session in "hydro" will contribute later to a period of quiet behavior on the ward.

Means for the enforcement of rules or of conformity to the daily pattern are ever present. The fenced-in section of the dayroom, called the Bullpen, where the more agitated, potentially assaultive patients are kept, is often used as a place of punishment. If someone does not want to go to dinner, he may be told that he will not get a chance to eat later. Seclusion is always available, both as a punishment for patients who "get out of hand" in the staff's opinion and as a protection for the catatonic patient who begins to shift from stupor to agitation. Hydro and "packs" also have a punishment value as well as a quieting one for those who are agitated, or make trouble for the staff. New patients soon find out that it is best to behave and conform to the regular pattern.

The typical daily pattern involves no element of surprise. Events can be anticipated well in advance. For the most part the patients sit and watch those few who move. Here the nurse's remark quoted earlier is very apt—"There are on every ward the doers, the watchers of the doers, and the watchers of the watchers." Recreational facilities are limited or nonexistent. Reading material is usually restricted to newspapers which the staff may bring in (primarily for themselves). Radio and television may be available but controlled in use because of the possible "exciting effect" they may have on patient behavior. Occupational therapy is absent except for the daily details of sweeping the ward and pushing the polishing blocks over the floor after supper, which are done by those patients who are known not to be troublesome and "are better off kept busy doing something." Therefore, a good share of the day is spent just sitting or walking up and down the ward.

Patient-staff relationships in terms of social interaction are almost nonexistent. Decisions are made by the attendant and orders given. There is no give and take about daily events, no opportunity for the patient to choose from a number of alternatives, no sharing by staff and patients of jokes, or plans, or even reminiscences. It is all one way.

Even the daily visit by the physician lacks the interpersonal interest that is usually to be found in doctor-patient relationships. The visitor learns that both patients and ward staff have come to refer to the visit as Galloping Rounds. At the appointed time each day the physician appears at the entrance to the ward, his presence signaled by the Lookout. Usually he is flanked by attendants or the supervising nurse, who will tell him which patients should be seen. Since the ward is so large, and there are many similar wards for which the physician has responsibility, it is impossible for him to know all the patients, or to see more than a few. Primarily, he deals with the little emergencies that arise, "dispensing a platitude with every poultice," lingers briefly at the charge attendant's desk, signs the orders, and leaves.

If the visitor returns to the ward frequently he will find everything in the same order each time, the withdrawn, passive, yet hostile faces of the patients, the Wall Standers and Bench Warmers in the same place. He gets a similar feeling after a visit to a museum, of types, of exhibits in order, of unchanging and unvaried pattern. Then he understands why the place of gestures and faces, of order and silence has been called a Museum Ward.

The Moving Ward

As our visitor walks on to the next ward he will be rather surprised to find so few patients there. The ward looks almost deserted. A question to the attendant who is present reveals that most of the patients are in various parts of the hospital, engaged in different recreational and occupational activities. The observer is told that he will have to come back to the ward at mealtime or in the evening in order to find the full roster of patients present. Even then, he could be disappointed, for some of the patients may be attending a movie or a weekly dance.

Not only does the ward look different because there are so few patients present, it also has a different ward geography. In one corner of the room there is a television set encircled by a group of chairs. Another corner is occupied by a pool table. The ward office is at the side and chairs of various kinds are scattered about the room. The rigid order of ward geography found on the Museum Ward is absent here, although there is order to the geography focused around the radio or TV sets, the pool table, and the magazine racks.

A question about the patients who can be seen on the ward brings the information that there are two kinds, the Goose Eggs and the Ward Helpers. The former are patients who show no sign of making a good enough adjustment for ward work or occupational therapy. The latter are valuable adjuncts to the housekeeping force and the care of other patients. Among the Goose Eggs one can recognize familiar types, the Bench Warmers, Sitters, and Standers, even a few Pacers. In addition, there is something new, the TV Addict, who sits in front of the television screen for hours, seemingly absorbed in everything that is shown. In terms of the previous classification the visitor will probably decide that most of these patients are Watchers of Doers.

The visitor notes that smoking is permitted, that the charge attendant may be out on the porch, that no patients are in restraint. The situation is so different in so many ways from the Museum Ward that our visitor's curiosity is aroused and he is eager to find out more from the staff about this kind of ward behavior. What are the reasons behind it? He learns that the patients who are away from the ward are in hospital industry or on a special "total push" program. Staff action is motivated by the belief that the social regression of the chronic psychotic patient can be arrested and overcome only by pushing him into continuous social contact with other patients and hospital personnel. In addition, the aim is to bring him into continuous contact with the kinds of activities that are part of life outside the hospital. The staff agree that if left to his own devices the patient would shrink farther from the world. It is assumed that only by constantly urging him to participate in situations from which he seeks to escape can he learn to handle these situations and improve his social adjustment. In the hope of counteracting regression, the plan is to have each patient daily face a specific schedule of activity; that is, work at some kind of regular job or spend a given amount of time in occupational therapy. He is supposed to make social contacts through participation in social events or attendance at recreational affairs such as dances, movies, or other gatherings. The program is a total push to overcome inertia, an emphasis on movement, hence the term "Moving Ward."

The daily program for those on a Moving Ward is planned with many of the needs of the patient in mind. A spot in the laundry or kitchen or on the maintenance crew of the grounds is ready-made for the physically able patient whose prognosis is poor but who is a potentially quiet worker. As an alternate to constant hydrotherapy or restraint, or both, a "pick and shovel," or "gravel pit" program is available for the chronically disturbed, young, muscular patient. For the quiet but chronic patient there is the sorting, sewing, and mending room or a job as a cafeteria helper. To benefit the small number of clinically more promising patients and those middle-aged and older patients who are not strong enough for steady hospital work, a number of recreational opportunities are available. These patients are granted library privileges and may engage in some handicrafts, art work, or gardening, as time permits. If they are not too tired from their day's work, or activities, they can also look forward to attending weekly dances or movies in the auditorium.

These activities take the patient off the ward for a good portion of each day, conducted as they are in outside shops on the hospital grounds. They give the patient opportunity for contact with many patients from other wards as well as a number of different staff members. The hope is that the world of his social contacts will therefore be increased, not only numerically but psychologically.

The visitor learns that a typical day on this ward begins with a 7:30 breakfast, followed by an hour devoted to ward cleaning and rounds. Then from 9:00 to 11:00 or 11:30 most of the patients leave the ward to take part in hospital industry, occupational therapy, or educational therapy, activities that are held in different buildings. After lunch is served, and a half-hour rest, all the patients except those in the hospital industry program go to sports activities for two hours. Those who were taking insulin treatment during the morning are scheduled for occupational, physical, and corrective therapy. From 3:30 until 5:30 all patients again have leisure time except for two days a week when the library cart is on the floor. On three evenings of the week movies or special educational programs are scheduled, on three there is time set aside for showers, and on Sunday night the time is devoted to recreation under the direction of "Special Services." This, indeed, is a different day from that experienced by the patients on the Museum Ward.

The daily schedule follows a regular pattern, set up well in advance and posted in the ward office. In addition, there is a sheet for each patient so that the amount of time he spends at occupational, recreational, corrective, educational, or physical therapy can be noted. For those who are on total push treatment their lives are run by the chart and they are constantly on the move, lining up to go to meals, or a job, or the auditorium, or the ball park. It is easy to see why Moving Ward is an exceedingly apt name.

Here is a ward that is half empty during most of the day, that has a great deal of equipment for recreation, that allows much more freedom of movement and interaction to those who remain on the ward. The question arises as to the need for control measures. The visitor is told that hydrotherapy and packs are always available and used occasionally, as is seclusion. The frequency of use, however, does not seem to be so great as on the Museum Ward. The ward staff express the opinion that this is due in part to the fact that many of the patients find an outlet for their energies in the round of their daily activities. For those who remain on the ward supervision can come from Patient Helpers and the staff can have more time to do things with them. The visitor is told also that these patients may not be so sick as those whom he has seen on other wards. Some of the staff, however, raise the question whether the fact that the patients appear less regressed is a function of the degree of their illness or a function of the stimulation and push on this ward.

Patient-staff interaction on this ward does take place. The only trouble is that there is very little time for it in the groups of patients who move all day long. Thus, although the possibility exists, it never develops into real relationship. The situation is different with the Goose Eggs and Patient Helpers. On the ward most of the time, they have the opportunity for continuous social interaction with the staff. They are second-class citizens, however, below those who are in hospital industry or on a total push program; thus, they do not get so much attention as time might permit.

After the order and conformity of the Museum Ward, the Moving Ward seems one of movement and permission. It is deceptive though, and the visitor wonders if the daily schedule of activity may not be as productive of conformity as the rules of the Museum Ward. He will puzzle over this for some time.

The Family Ward

Our visitor's reception on the next ward is different from any he has had yet. The patients and staff greet him; he does not have to greet them. He senses that they act like different people but he knows patients are as ill here as on the other wards. As he develops a feeling for the patients and ward events, he may have the impression that the activity is like that in a small rural community where life goes on unhurried. On closer observation he notices a variety of interpersonal relationships that resemble those in an old-fashioned household with many children, grandchildren, and relatives. It is almost like a big family. There is a sizable group of younger and older ward veterans who constitute a relatively stable ward society, around which transient patients come and go.

There is a deceptive normalcy to the behavior of patients on this chronic ward. The visitor notes an informality and intimacy among patients and personnel that he did not see on the other wards. He also observes a differentiation of social roles that he did not see so clearly on the Museum or Moving Wards.

The observer soon picks out the Ward Hero. Often he functions as the Wise Man or Ward Diagnostician to the other patients. Usually a ward veteran, with many years of experience with staff and patients behind him, he is well informed about the differences in degree and type of illness of each patient. Able to see early signs of returning agitation in a withdrawn patient, he reports to the attendant what he finds. Subsequently he may help the attendant persuade this person to move to a less stimulating part of the ward. When a new patient arrives, the Ward Hero is often the one who lends him emotional support by introducing him to the various ward groups. From time to time he may even check the patient's progress in relation to various ward cliques to see how he is getting along.

When a disagreement between two patients threatens to end in a quarrel or real brawl, the Ward Hero will attempt to forestall it. Knowing the other patients well, he is very sensitive to the "manicky" patient who is approaching recovery. He knows at this time the patient may want especially to express his need for leadership and seek to organize the "boys with the sideway looks and backward glances." He also knows that this patient would only stir things up with his methods and may help to steer him to other tasks that will help to drain off his excess energy.

The Ward Hero feels that he is not just another patient. His knowledge of the ward and its occupants makes him a staff ally. He has made illness his occupation and, thus, he can deny the existence of his own illness or at least its dangers. His reward is the role of Ward Hero.

The Ward Clown or Fool is as essential in this patient community as the Hero. He is "a weak one," often avoided by other patients at meals and bedtime because of his bizarre manners. Yet he has a repertoire of funny stories and he entertains patients as he impersonates the frailties or mannerisms of others. At such times they can laugh at him, or when he is intentionally clumsy. They need him because he provides comic relief; but they do not laugh with him. He reminds them of what not to be, if they want to be normal.

The visitor soon learns something about the perennial problem patients of the ward. One of several such "villains" that may come to his attention is the Con Man. He shams and ingratiates himself with the others. He mulcts the Clown who believes in him but he cannot abscond very far with the Clown's cherished ball of tinfoil before he is stopped by the attendant. He may try to persuade an aged patient to give up his favorite rocking chair in return for getting him up and helping him to the bathroom. However, he often meets his Waterloo at the hands of his traditional adversary, the Shopkeeper.

The Shopkeeper is the ward scoundrel who has found a means to be systematically dishonest with his fellow patients. He is an expert at exchanging pieces of string or paper for a cigarette, tobacco, pipe cleaners, and other minor ward valuables. Unashamed of these one-sided exchanges, he both intrigues and repels the other patients with his devious and socially unacceptable ways. He is often the object of serious moral concern to an elderly patient "who has religion in a bad way." Known to all as the Preacher, he tries to expose the Shopkeeper while the latter tries to unfrock him. They make a strange pair, indeed, but both are tolerated and are even important members of the ward.

Although many patients may no longer believe in God, they are silent when the Preacher reads from his Bible and prays over a patient before he goes to shock treatment. They are glad and grateful when he tries to reform the Shopkeeper. They may think of him as a character and even as a comic, but they do not ask him to stop offering prayers.

There is little difficulty in recognizing these patients. Since all conform to familiar social types, they are known to the ward by colloquial terms. They lend the appearance of organization to what at a glance is only a crowd of patients, but most importantly, they help to create a world that is similar to the world outside. Thus, most patients are prevented from remaining complete strangers to each other for long.

In the fashion of the large family, staff and patients alike may refer to one patient as the Household Drudge. He is a devout worker, who makes his ward his stronghold, and who can be heard telling another patient, "My work is my pleasure." Another patient is known as the Gadabout or Errand Boy. He seems to have a constant desire to visit with other patients and an insatiable curiosity about happenings off the ward. Since he usually has ground parole, he is ever hankering for errands that give him an opportunity to practice his reportorial bent.

As a rule, there are several ward patients who are called the Silent, Stubborn Ones. They have reputed deep emotions and other patients and staff suggest that it is best to leave them alone unless they come out of hiding. The ward family seems to expect them to seek each other's company, as if it granted them the right to dissent from its way of life. The visitor hears a nurse express herself to the effect that they may be in mute rebellion against those who seek to make the ward into the image of the outside.

The ward family has a name for almost every patient. There is the Whiner and Complainer, who always tries to shirk his duties. Another is referred to as the Informer or Tattletale. He carries stories about other patients to the staff, and he sidles up to supervisory personnel on their daily rounds to inform on the ward staff. Frequently, he has a run-in with the Go-between, who generally is well liked by both patients and staff. The latter's role is appreciated because he tries to settle differences of opinion about necessary ward chores and the like, as well as interceding on behalf of his fellow patients with the charge nurse or aide.

In addition to this description of the Family Ward in terms of role classifications, the visitor will carry away impressions about certain of the social processes that run through ward life. One of these is the emphasis on cooperation. The limited living facilities and comforts, the restricted space, have put a premium on cooperation. By and large the patients know that what they can do depends on what others do and plan to do. Also, the staff appear to foster and maintain this attitude in a number of ways. For example, they seem eager to preserve an equable division of labor and of special functions according to the ability, interest, and age of the patients. In such planning they are not averse to soliciting the tacit support of the ward veterans, so that there is a good deal of interdependence between patients and staff. Both have a sense of belonging.

Along with a spirit of cooperation and helpfulness there is also much competition and contention. For the control of this behavior there are both subtle and overt forms of social sanction. The patients know that they cannot order each other around as they might sometimes wish. They realize that there would be resistance from other patients to their attempts at aggression, also a stern reproof and perhaps loss of privileges from the nurse or charge aide. In addition, the patients punish the "sassy" patient with silence or anger when he tries to pick on the Wee One and whenever he flaunts the authority of the ward veterans. If someone does not behave properly, disdain is shown in the faces and voices of the others. There are unwritten rules for behavior that both staff and patients understand and share in the enforcement.

Not only are the spirit of cooperation and the social controls analogous to those found in large family life, but so also is the humor. Patients seem to enjoy the many occasions they have to laugh at their elders behind their backs. The visiting doctors on rounds are called the Travelers. A prim, skinny, rule-conscious supervisor is dubbed the Yardstick. Laughter peals when the Clown mimics a bespectacled and squinting doctor, or a nurse who is generously endowed in certain physical assets but otherwise inadequate.

Others engage in banter about their fate, commenting facetiously that the length of hospital stay is really only a matter of luck or influence. There is blasphemous laughter about a patient's lack of normal maleness. An old paretic patient, forever wearing an inane smile, and a garb of swathed sheets because of his incontinence, is derisively known as the Bloomer Girl. The garrulous paranoid patient whose health is complicated by hypertension is diagnosed as having high blood pressure of the lips. A ward veteran regards his lack of results from maintenance shock as his bad batting average. The ward cynic announces to the visitor that death outplays anything that medicine can do. Indeed, the smiles and laughter seem to make sport of illness and death.

Such, in brief, is the Family Ward, a place of sharing, of belongingness, of security from the outside world.

REFLECTIONS ON THREE PATTERNS OF WARD CARE

The pictures we have drawn of the Museum, Moving, and Family Wards have been merely sketches and, as we stated earlier, they are composites or "ideal types." When seen in a hospital setting, they usually exist as variations of our description.

However, practically every large hospital has one or more of them, developed out of the need for compromise between inadequate facilities and an overload of patients, or from serious experimental endeavor or permissive concern with ill people. We feel it is important, therefore, at this juncture to point out certain features of each pattern that are important in patient care.

In the first case, the Museum Ward, the care of the patient is management through the use of rigid rules. The emphasis is on maintenance of the ward and on control functions of the staff. The prevailing pattern is prevention and security, rules and an enforced patient submission. In the Moving Ward care is really controlled treatment through the manipulation of the patient, the pushing into a schedule of activity. The prevailing pattern is activity and decision by the staff, and an induced lack of patient initiative. In the Family Ward care comes through ward roles and responsibility training, with a pattern of discipline and decision-making that is largely maintained by and for the patients themselves. The pattern is informality, hard work, and service for both patients and staff.

Another feature of staff-patient relationships lies in the distinction between ill and normal. The distinction is sharpest on the Museum Ward and the social distance between staff and patients is great, exemplified in the remark of one physician that his ward was filled with "woody, old vegetables." The distance is due partly to the fact that the Legend of Chronicity is accepted here and the restoration of patients to health or a better hospital adjustment is not usually expected. The distinction between ill and normal is less sharp but still present on the Moving Ward. It is preserved because the staff do not have an adequate opportunity to form lasting relationships with the patients and because they still retain the exclusive power of decision. However, the lessened social distance results in part from the fact that the Legend of Chronicity is avoided because staff pretend that it does not exist and an improvement in social adjustment is anticipated. The distinction between ill and normal is minimized on the Family Ward, for here the staff adopt the attitude of being an integral part of the ward patient universe. They are inclined to accept the patient for what he is now, stressing the need for normalcy even in illness. The Legend of Chronicity is not seen as a problem because in the climate of the Family Ward chronic deviant behavior is often viewed as eccentricity.

The three ward types may also be considered from the point of view of their effect on the patient. Emotional isolation is the result of the atmosphere of the Museum Ward. Unable to form lasting social relationships with either the staff or the other patients, the individual is driven more and more within himself. The world of fantasy is lived in, not just believed in. The result is a sense of nonidentity, expressed by one of the more articulate patients when he said, "I'm nobody and going no place . . . like the others here."

A patient on the Moving Ward also has the problem of forming lasting social contacts with ward mates or staff but it is not in the context of forced withdrawal. Rather it is in the context of forced movement. It results in more of an emotional confusion than isolation. The danger to the patient results from the fact that he has little or no choice in his activities and may be pushed into certain activities before he is ready for them. This situation of emotional confusion was characterized by a patient on a Moving Ward this way: "I'm something all right, always doing things, but I can't tell where I am going. Being busy at being happy, I guess."

The patient who is a member of a Family Ward has a certain freedom from total supervision and planning by the staff, plus some stimulation from the social situation outside the hospital. The positive effect is a supportive one, enabling the patient to work at his own speed in sorting out the complex problems of his retreat from the world. The potential negative effect is that the individual will be so dominated by the group that he may be absorbed by the group and lose what little initiative he has for making a better social adjustment beyond the ward setting. Such a situation can be seen in many of the ward veterans. The effect has been summed up in the statement of a patient: "I'm doing my job here O.K., but there's too darn much family stuff for me; gets on my nerves, see."

Finally, there is a varying effect on staff members in each of the three ward situations. In the Museum Ward it is so easy for the nurse or attendant to lose sight of the fact that the patients are human beings, not just types or bits of movement in the ward geography. The situation also provides the staff an outlet for unspent aggressive urges, especially those that may arise from the frustration of dealing with long-term mental illness. On a Museum Ward it is difficult to channel aggression into productive activity.

The staff of a Moving Ward may have a different attitude toward their patients, believing that they can get well and need to be pushed, but the danger lies in the ritual of motion. On the one hand, so much time can be spent in keeping records and being busy with the schedule that the individual can be overlooked or forgotten. On the other hand, the schedule of activities can become an end in itself, or a substitute gratification for goal-directed patterns of care.

Perhaps the greatest danger on the Family Ward is that of inertia. Some patients will recover from a psychosis by themselves if given enough time and a suitable hospital atmosphere. Others need steady direction and urging to bring them back to reality and normal social contacts. By allowing the patients to have more freedom of choice in their activities the staff may lose sight of some of their own responsibilities to the mentally ill, as far as providing the extra drive to direct the patient's goals beyond the confines of the ward community. It is easy to become complacent in a situation of this kind.

SOCIAL REMOTIVATION AS A PATTERN OF PATIENT CARE

Up to this point we have emphasized four factors which bear on the care and treatment of long-term mental patients: (1) the reality of everyday operating problems, those connected with budgets, buildings, shortage of personnel, and abundance of patients; (2) the tendency to classify patients according to behavioral characteristics or place in the ward scheme rather than by diagnostic labels; (3) the presence of the Legend of Chronicity and its deadening effect on active treatment programs; (4) the variety in patterns of ward care that have developed, the Museum, Moving, and Family Wards, each with some strengths yet many drawbacks in relation to patient improvement.

We turn now to a different approach to the long-term mental patient, one we have characterized as social remotivation. Its primary feature lies in a set of attitudes, toward the patient and toward the treatment process. In terms of the patient, social remotivation requires the acceptance of the patient as a worthwhile individual, capable of improvement, regardless of the degree of observable deterioration. Furthermore, its aim is to have the patient come to accept himself as well as help him to be acceptable to others. Under the philosophy of social remotivation the patient is granted certain rights, first, to as active treatment as possible, the most beneficial program for his particular problems. At the same time he is given the right of choice occasionally, to be alone if he wishes, yet be respected.

Social remotivation seeks to mobilize the entire ward routine and program for therapeutic ends. Once the patient has been accepted as worthwhile and as having potential for growth, the daily activities of ward life can take on new meaning. Rather than deadening routine, they can become worthwhile learning experiences if they represent graded levels of achievement in the needs of the ward as a community. Thus, the social milieu of the ward is mobilized to bring out latent energies toward health, reinforce them through a series of social rewards, looking toward an improved hospital adjustment or eventual return to the community.

To return to the four factors noted at the beginning of this section, social remotivation as a pattern of care has to accept the reality of everyday operating problems, at least for the present. In fact, to us one of the important features is that in spite of crowded conditions and inadequate numbers of physicians, nurses, and aides, encouraging programs of ward care can be developed. The cases described in the following chapters occurred in large state hospitals where administrative problems were ever present.

Social classification of patients can be useful rather than detrimental if placed in the proper perspective and with positive ends in view. In colloquial language, social classification isn't bad if you know what to do with it. The action component of the definition is therefore important. In certain ward situations, for example, the Museum Ward, social classification is used primarily as a way of sorting patients in order to keep the ward routine operating. In social remotivation the classification is used to emphasize positive patient roles, or those aspects of patient behavior that can contribute to improved skills in interpersonal relations. It is never used to emphasize negative personality characteristics, as in the case of Drips and Drags or Goose Eggs.

"Beyond the Legend of Chronicity," a phrase used as the title of the last chapter, indicates that social remotivation cannot accept the definition of chronic that emphasizes hopelessness or minimal expectations for patient improvement. In fact, social remotivation is the antithesis of the Legend of Chronicity.

Finally, remotivation draws from the Museum, Moving, and Family Wards those features of each which can be used for the benefit of the patient. For example, the rules and authority of the Museum Ward may be most valuable in reducing anxiety of some patients about the force of urges within themselves. Even as the growing child becomes anxious without some setting of limits by his parents, so the psychotic patient may be overwhelmed by a completely permissive environment. Rules and order are used, however, with the needs of particular patients constantly in mind, to benefit ill people, rather than for the ends of control and conformity alone.

The push and direction found on the Moving Ward are valuable assets to counteract the natural withdrawal tendencies of the person who cannot face the problems of the world. Without help by the staff toward the reestablishment of worthwhile relations with others, many patients would merely rigidify their withdrawal patterns. Push and direction are used to build a confidence in self, not only to make the person acceptable to others; and caution must be exercised that movement does not become an end in itself.

On the Family Ward the emphasis on social structure, the development of varied roles, and the closeness of staff and patients can contribute much toward health. These features are utilized in social remotivation, but with the constant reminder that the hospital ward must not become a second home that precludes interest on taking up life again outside.

In Chapter 9 we shall return again to a discussion of the process of social remotivation. In the intervening chapters descriptive cases of the ways in which remotivation has been put into practice on a variety of wards, and in many different hospitals, will give the reader an opportunity to think about it in practical rather than abstract terms.

3. The Habit Training Ward

W<small>ARD</small> J-4 <small>AT</small> L<small>YNWOOD STATE HOSPITAL</small>, a closed ward for chronic male patients, is clean and homelike. No offensive odors are present even though many of the patients are old and quite regressed. There are few restraints necessary and all patients are fully clothed, including shoes. A small but steady flow of discharges takes place from this ward to other wards where patients show an improved ability for social adjustment. It has not always been as described here; in fact, until recently it was classified as one of the hospital's back wards. At the present time it presents one side of a contrast so striking as to be almost unbelievable.

A few years ago this ward was not a pretty sight nor a pleasant place to visit. Built to house 70 patients it had a population of 90, ranging in age from eighteen to eighty-nine years of age. Sixty per cent of these patients had been in Lynwood State Hospital for more than fifteen years, while only 10 per cent had been there less than five years. The psychological condition of the patients was one of severe deterioration, but of those whose diagnosis could be identified 18 were mental defectives, 8 were paretics, and 7 were epileptics. Diagnostically speaking, they "ran from one type of illness to the other."

The behavior of the ward in general was characterized by intermittent bursts of excitement, necessitating the use of continuous restraint for a third of the patients. These 30 were nude, tearing clothes off immediately if any were put on them. One patient had been existing with wrist restraints in a shower room under a shower for more than a year because of incontinence. In fact, most of the patients were incontinent in urinary excretion at one time or another during the day or night. Nearly a third were stool smearers.

54

During the day the patients could be found sitting on the same chairs, rockers, or benches, or lying in the same spot on the floor. Eighteen of them were mute except for grunts or infrequent bursts of screaming. Eight were constant talkers or autistic murmurers. Numerous patients ate with their fingers, ignoring the spoon placed before them. Twenty of them had to be tray-fed, and 10 even spoon-fed because they were so regressed that they showed no interest in food.

In addition, the physical condition of the patients was poor, with a prevalence of dependent edema of the legs, skin rashes, ringworm, and halitosis. The incidence of the last named was highest, with an extremely poor condition of mouth, gums, and teeth due to poor oral hygiene. There was a steady flow of patients to the medical and surgical wards because of these disorders, as well as the regular occurrence of injuries.

The ward itself was untidy, actually dirty, "literally swimming in urine," as some of the staff said. The walls were olive drab and mouldy green, with nothing bright or colorful to break the monotonous expanse. In short, it was truly a back ward, smelly and depressing.

The impetus for a change in this situation came from a number of sources. The idea was initiated by the clinical director, Dr. Bates, who had just returned from a survey of state hospitals, where he had seen the efforts of other people directed toward improving the condition of some of their back wards. He felt that if they could do it, so could the staff of his hospital. In addition to this, Lynwood State Hospital had just begun an aide training program under the direction of Miss Lane, R.N. One of the important tasks in that kind of program was to teach the habit training of patients. For this, one needed demonstration wards where various schemes could be tried and where student aides could gain experience. The pressure was present, therefore, to select a ward in the hospital for improvement in habit training, or its innovation where none existed.

Other factors helped to lead to the selection of Ward J-4. One of these has already been mentioned, the steady run of patients to the medical and surgical service because of poor physical care on the ward and frequency of accidents. This was a drain on valuable hospital space and time. The other reason could be found in the laundry. Here an informal study had been conducted concerning the laundry load in pounds per patient. It was no surprise to find that this was much higher on the untidy wards, especially on J-4.

Accordingly, in March of 1951 plans were drawn and activities begun for remotivation on this ward. As a way of illustrating the feeling of the staff at the beginning, some selections from a reconstructed interview with Miss Lane and some of the aides may be interesting.

> When we started this work we were naturally concerned about whether any good could come out of working with such patients. We had heard of people trying it with women patients in some hospitals and getting someplace. But you know how men are, they get the boarding house habit and would rather die than lift a finger to help straighten things out.
>
> Anyway, we did not know how many people we would need for the job. The noisy and violent patients and the soilers took up all the time of the regular personnel. The other patients were simply there and forgotten; there was no time for contact with them by staff. They just sat around the walls, lay on the floor in the same place day in and day out. Once in a while they'd take a mind to bite another patient or an attendant, for no reason at all, you know, and then they would be still for quite a spell. If you tried to talk to them they were apt to spit and cuss you everlastingly. So most attendants left them alone.
>
> All this made the decision to start anything real hard, especially since we wanted a female charge aide; and you know how many hospital people feel about having a female on the male side. After much opposition we got it through—told everybody that men are likely to behave better with women even if they are real sick.

One of the first graduates of the psychiatric aide class, Mrs. Cosgrove, was selected as the new charge aide for J-4. This proved to be a happy choice, for much of the subsequent change depended on her firm, friendly manner and her tireless enthusiasm for her mission. Happily married and the mother of two grown daughters, she brought stability and patience to a situation that she knew would change but slowly.

Mrs. Cosgrove started the psychiatric aide class with some experience in taking care of mental patients. During the Great Depression both she and her husband had gone to work at Lynwood in order to keep their home and family together. Even after Mr. Cosgrove could return to his trade, his wife stayed on until they both decided that their growing family needed Mrs. Cosgrove's attention. Later she accepted a job with the student health service of a medical school in the city, the short hours permitting her to be at home when her daughters returned from school.

When both children had married, Mr. and Mrs. Cosgrove took a belated honeymoon to the West Coast, then on their return felt they could now do what they both wanted most, work at Lynwood again. This would give them the type of work they liked, as well as enable them to have more time together. Both enrolled in the first psychiatric aide class. Although Mrs. Cosgrove considered herself a good attendant, she realized after a few sessions how little she really knew about caring for the mentally ill patient. And now, she never tires of telling about how much she learned from the course in terms of the approach to different types of patients, tolerance, and general care of the mentally ill.

It is perhaps worth noting that both Mr. and Mrs. Cosgrove have always been active in church and school affairs as well as community social activities. When their children were young, their backyard was a playground for all the children in the neighborhood. They never seemed too busy to take time for play or the supervision of games. Nowadays they like to hunt and fish, to square dance, and to take part in various kinds of community work.

We have digressed to some extent here because the personality of the charge aide had so much to do with the eventual success of habit training, a fact which we hope will become apparent as the story of efforts on J-4 unfolds. We can turn now to a fuller exposition of that story.

In its physical structure Ward J-4 is like many other mental hospital wards across the country, consisting of a central corridor with dormitories, dining room, and shower room opening off

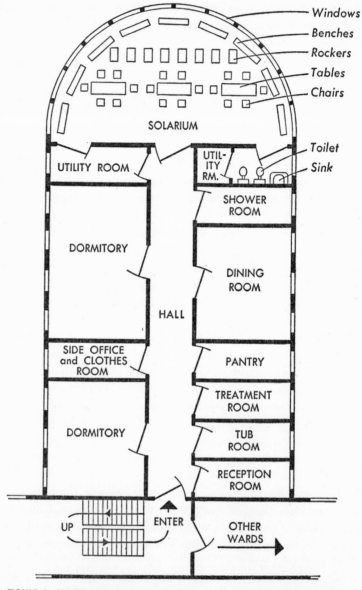

FIGURE 1. FLOOR PLAN OF MALE WARD J-4, LYNWOOD STATE HOSPITAL

from it. The general diagram can be seen in Figure 1. Benches and odd heavy chairs are found along each side of the hall and in the solarium. Here the benches line the windows, with rockers and chairs in rows filling up the rest of the space along with three heavy tables. It should be noted that there is only one toilet, containing two seats and a washbowl. In addition, the shower room has some large circular wash basins. The kitchen facilities in the form of a pantry are rather primitive for the number of people to be served, but are adequate. A cafeteria style service is utilized at meals.

It is important to keep this physical description in mind, for it played a prominent role in the problems that had to be faced. There were only two toilet seats for 90 patients, 80 of whom were incontinent at some time during a twenty-four hour period. Any program of habit training relative to excretory functions would need to take this into consideration, a formidable task in itself, to say nothing of keeping clothes on, encouraging better eating habits, and keeping patients clean.

In spite of the many obstacles facing her, a habit training routine in each of these areas was started the day that Mrs. Cosgrove took charge of the ward. The routine had as its objectives to keep each patient involved in all the things that went to make up his daily living, to raise the patients to a higher and more pleasant level of living, and to hope for an occasional restoration of at least some of the younger patients. The schedule included toilet training every two hours, daily brushing of teeth, washing of face and hands, combing of hair, dressing and wearing clothes and shoes, using regular table silverware, doing ward jobs, and taking part in recreation. It was Mrs. Cosgrove's responsibility to plan the program and supervise its accomplishment with the aides on her shift, as well as on the other shifts. Of necessity, the routine had to be fixed and unvarying. The staff realized that for these patients a solid routine provided something to cling to, in the same way that children need to know that there are certain times set aside for different events during the day. As would be expected, it took some time for the procedure to shake down into its present form. For the first few months, Mrs. Cosgrove and the aides did little else but get patients to do something or stop doing things. They coaxed, they tried being stern, they mentioned unheard-of privileges. They tried to get patients to initiate things, such as pushing a broom, or putting on clothes, or using better table manners. They ate with the patients and brought in extra patient help from other wards to assist them.

The problems involved in establishing the habit training routine were not all the fault of the patients. The staff had some problems of their own, fears that they might lose control over the situation and some patients might escape or injure other patients, fears that the program might not work out.

After three or four months there was a feeling that the patients were better, at least both staff and patients seemed to have more confidence in each other. Learning to know each other better meant that mistrust was giving way to understanding. Patients told the staff that they were kinder people and staff began to think that now they could start reducing restraints.

Progress was slow, but after about nine months patients began to help each other, mostly because they wanted to please the aides and Mrs. Cosgrove. Finally, this seemed to turn into a genuine thoughtfulness for each other. They still talked like sick people, stilted and rambling, but at least they talked more; and they tended to listen to those who spoke to them, and not just to fantasy voices. This all meant that the work that had to be done on the ward became more interesting to the patients and Mrs. Cosgrove could begin assigning jobs in accordance with patients' capabilities.

Things had come a long way by the end of a year. It was not necessary all the time to tell patients what to do; often they would come to ask what needed to be done, or even start a job on their own initiative. The staff made a point of not asking anyone to do a job just for the sake of doing something, for they thought that such was just busy work and not therapeutically helpful. Slowly the patients came to realize that there was a good reason for doing everything. The result of this work interest by the patients was more leisure time for everyone, because the chores got done faster. That meant that the staff then had time really to think about ways that they could brighten the ward hours with entertainment and occupational therapy.

In order not to get ahead of our story, we should describe in more detail various aspects of the habit training routine. Perhaps the most crucial and at the same time the most interesting part of this was toilet training. We have indicated the need for something to be done as well as the real obstacles that would have to be overcome, yet Mrs. Cosgrove devised an ingenious solution. All patients had toilet drill every two hours. At that time they assembled in the solarium and sat down on the chairs or benches that were placed there in rows (see ward diagram in Figure 1). Then in order, one by one, the patients moved to the toilet, of their own accord or aided by an attendant or patient helper. During the process Mrs. Cosgrove would take a position in the middle of the solarium, just inside the entrance from the hallway. Looking at the position of the patients and watching her work, one almost had the feeling that it was similar to the conductor of an orchestra. At first, the patients went through the drill as much out of curiosity as anything, because it was a break in the monotonous routine to which they were so accustomed. However, it was not easy and took nearly an hour and a half to complete the routine, using three student aides and the charge aide. By the time the ward was visited in connection with this study, some two years after habit training began, the procedure required only about forty-five minutes, and incontinence on the ward was no longer a problem. Also, it could be handled by one aide with the assistance of patient helpers.

When the habit training therapy began, a third of the patients had to relearn to wear clothes and nearly one-half to wear shoes. Clothing was being torn up and destroyed so fast in various ways that there was not always enough to go around. The change to clothes was a gradual one for the nude patients. At first, they wore strong hospital pants that were like BVD's, and no underpants, so that they could go to the toilet faster, without having to fuss with belts. After six months or so of this they were able to graduate to regular overalls.

It should be noted that once Mrs. Cosgrove had the dressing routine established to the point where most or all of the patients would wear clothes, she introduced variety in dress by obtaining clothes from rummage sales and other similar sources. This was a stimulus to the visitors and they began to contribute to the clothes variety on the ward.

A good illustration of the problem faced in clothing habits can be found in the case of Mr. Gaines, a mental defective patient. He presented a particularly trying problem from the standpoint of keeping him dressed. He had been in restraints for some time and when these were removed, he would have to be redressed as many as *twenty times* in a single *hour*. Gradually he improved to the point where several months later he required redressing only about six times a day. At the time of visit he stayed dressed all day, with no need of restraint, and was participating in scheduled ward activities.

Clothing is now being marked not only with the ward number but with the patient's name as well. A clothesroom has been set aside in which each patient has his own shelf, marked with his name, this room being under the supervision of Mr. Urwin, one of the schizophrenic patients. He takes great pride in seeing that the clothes are folded neatly and placed in individual compartments, and also that coats and dress trousers are put on hangers.

In the area of eating habits many patients were being fed from trays because they were too untidy to come to the dining room, while others had to be spoon-fed, owing to their lack of interest in food. We noted that in the beginning the staff ate with the patients, applying individual effort to those patients who needed help. The difficulty can best be shown by referring to Mr. Le Conte, a catatonic schizophrenic patient who was being spoon-fed. Taking him to the dining room availed nothing; his interest in food no longer existed. However, the staff persisted in taking him to the table for each meal until he no longer resisted, although he would not feed himself. Patiently, day after day, the spoon was put in his hand and guided to his mouth till finally he began eating by himself. It took eighteen months of perseverance before this was accomplished, and a knife and fork could be added to his table setting. Through such procedures a change in eating habits was brought about so that at the time of visit the majority of patients ate with knives and forks.

The remaining acute problem was that of odor. Those who have had experience with back wards will know whereof we speak; for others description will never quite suffice. When Mrs. Cosgrove began her work the smell was almost overpowering, a constant source of complaint for all those who came in contact with the ward. The method of attack was the scrubbing of every inch of the ward each day with soap and water. This was no easy task at first because there were so few patient helpers, most of those who were available having been brought in from other wards. With the slow improvement in patient contact and interest as well as the success of the toilet training, the problem of odors and keeping the ward clean became less acute. It is interesting that Mrs. Cosgrove comments that some of her best ward workers turned out to be those who had been "smearers." One of these, after constant attention, began to give up his interest in playing with dirt in the corners in favor of helping Mrs. Cosgrove and another patient wash walls, windows, and benches. Some five months later he discarded his reluctance to take a shower and began to wash himself without urging.

One other illustration might be cited here. Mr. White, who had been nude when the habit training began, readily put on clothing but continued to have trouble getting to the toilet without soiling. One of the older patients who had adjusted to the new ward routine adopted him and kept urging him to show Mrs. Cosgrove that he could improve. After some months he moved to the center of the hall one day where Mrs. Cosgrove could see him, opened his fly, then his belt, began to squall, and looked over his shoulder. With quick presence of mind, Mrs. Cosgrove said, "Okay, I'll take you to the bathroom." This was the first time he had ever asked to go to the toilet, but from then on improvement was rapid and soon he was adopting patients himself and helping them in the routine.

In addition to the perseverance of the staff, the key to the successful carrying out of these efforts could be found in two administrative actions, the development of a strict schedule and the evolvement of a scheme of job classification. The latter had two parts, a patient description chart according to ratings of ability, and a description of job roles graded according to difficulty.

Factors to be considered in the rating of patients can be seen in Chart 1. Mrs. Cosgrove posted this in the ward office so that all shifts could become familiar with it and learn how to assess the potential value of different patients. She hoped that this would encourage staff on other shifts to select patients for special attention and retraining, once they began to show progress in bladder and bowel control.

When the ward was visited in 1954 there were 7 patients who had an A rating, 6 with B rating, 5 with C rating, and approximately 40 with D rating. The rest of the ward members were the unemployed. When the program was initiated, most of the patients would have been classified in the last category.

CHART 1. CLASSIFICATION OF PATIENTS FOR WARD EMPLOY-ABILITY ON WARD J-4

Rating	Overall criterion	Evaluation points
A	Patient will do job regularly once he is taught the routine	1. Patient can work with attention 2. A tidy dresser 3. Cleans self 4. A regular eater 5. Walks with other patients of his own will 6. Knows other patients by name 7. Can handle brooms, etc., appropriately
B	Patient has to be watched on the job, at least in the beginning of assigned work; usually manages to complete the job on his own	1. May not get along well with other patients; resents being interrupted in his work 2. Usually taciturn and not interested in other patients 3. Generally has tidy habits but needs occasional reminding
C	Patient has to be watched at all times while working on an assigned task; or requires the continuous example of an attendant working beside him on the same job	1. Speaks only when spoken to, or chatters to an imaginary person 2. Easily distracted 3. Handles tools clumsily or cannot handle them at all without guidance 4. May be untidy about personal hygiene and clothing, but otherwise is habit trained
D	Patients who may be called occasional workers "when the mood hits them"; and those who, though still disturbed, are able and willing to do one task well in the company of other patients or alone, such as mopping floor, pushing polishing block, etc.	

Arranged in order of presumed skill and interpersonal competence was a series of ward jobs to which individual patients were assigned. This is shown in Chart 2. The list of patients assigned to each category was also posted so that those on other shifts could keep track of the work order. This avoided the possibility of giving patients assignments out of turn. It also prevented certain patients, such as a Con Man, taking advantage of

CHART 2. JOB CLASSIFICATION SHEET FOR WARD J-4

Job description and grouping	Number of patients working
Group 1	
Toilet drill assistants	2
Tooth-brushing routine assistant	1
Morning care assistants	
Assistant face washer	1
Assistant hair combers	2
Assistant for keeping the patient line straight	1
Assistant patient bathers	2
Total	9
Group 2	
Clothesroom men	2
Pantry men	3
Dining-room men	4
Total	9
Group 3	
Laundry man (preparation of clothes)	1
Laundry men (washing)	2
Cleaners for toilet and shower room	3
Cleaner for hydrotherapy room	1
South dorm bed makers and floor moppers	3
North dorm bed makers and floor moppers	1
Total	11
Group 4	
Solarium scrubbers	7
Solarium bench washers	6
Hall cleaner	1
Side rooms and front rooms bed maker	1
Side rooms and front rooms floor mopper	1
South dorm scrubbers (Monday only)	7
North dorm scrubbers (Wednesday only)	7
Total	30

an aide's ignorance and palming off his job on another patient, especially one who might not be ready yet for the responsibility.

The daily activity schedule of Ward J-4 began at 6:50 in the morning. The time from then until eight o'clock was given over to brushing of teeth, face washing, hair combing, and breakfast. There were two sittings of 45 patients each at breakfast, two patients being spoon-fed and two on a special diet tray. These four patients were cared for by other patients. Toilet drill took place at eight o'clock. At 8:45 there was a twenty-minute walk for all patients except those on working details or apprentice details, the latter commencing their jobs at this time. The walk, in the solarium or outdoors when the weather was pleasant, often was led by one of the patients. The next period of activity, from 9:05 to 10:00, was scheduled for occupational and recreational therapy. Nearly half the patients were considered able to enter into this program, which was supervised by Mrs. Cosgrove and a student aide. It consisted of work with wood and clay, picture painting, and work on a rug frame. The object was twofold: to make things that would improve the appearance of the ward and that could be given to visitors. Patients not participating in this activity might be engaged in a special ward project, or could read books or magazines, listen to music, or watch TV.

At the time of visit many of the trusted ward patient workers were engaged in a wall-painting project. This was headed by Mr. Orr, a disturbed and obstreperous patient at the beginning of habit training, who was now the "master painter" putting his long forgotten trade to good use. There was a good chance, the observer was told, that he might soon join the hospital painters on a real job.

The television set had been presented to the ward by visitors in appreciation of all that Mrs. Cosgrove had done to bring happiness to, and a better way of living for, the patients. Mrs. Cosgrove had also introduced recorded music during recreation hours, both for background and listening, finding that popular music, hillbilly music, and waltzes brought out most of the patients.

Toilet drill was held again at ten o'clock, by which time the solarium had been scrubbed and patients had been given their medications. This was followed by lunch at 10:45 for most of the patients, the patient helpers and part of the ward attendants eating at 11:30.

Another toilet drill was scheduled for 12:15, followed by an hour and a quarter of various patient activities. The extent of variety possible here would depend on the number of personnel available on the ward, but frequently a recreational therapist would come with a punching bag, beanbags, and the like, which the patients enjoyed a great deal. At the end of this period, 2:15, there was another toilet drill, then sweep-up time and preparations for the evening shift.

The rest of the afternoon and the evening were devoted to toilet drill at two-hour intervals, activities in between, dinner, and visitors in the evening (twice a week). Showers or baths were given three times a week, except in the case of the few remaining untidy patients who had a shower every day.

In addition to the occupational roles assigned to the patients, certain of them were given added responsibilities, and consequently added status, in becoming physical symptom and patient behavior spotters. This assignment was made to those patients who were classified in Group 1 jobs (see Chart 2), nine in number at the time of visit. Under the heading physical symptoms, they were trained to watch for early skin conditions, weight loss, swollen legs, poor eating habits, and poor condition of the mouth, gums, or teeth. Under the heading patient behavior, they were taught to make a rating of appearance on the basis of the tidiness of hair and beard, cleanliness of face, fingernails, and hands, cleanliness of trousers, jacket and shoes, attention to trouser buttons, and finally, early signs of disturbed behavior.

Such training was begun gradually, with concentration first on the accurate observation of physical symptoms. Later they were asked to go farther and in effect become the standard setters of ward behavior and appearance. Also, the principle of the sick caring for the sick, which was so important on the Family Ward, gave a sense of identity and purpose to the ward. In addition, this helped to reduce the number of cases going to the medical and surgical wards, one of the early problems on J-4.

Rewards for good work were partly inherent in the situation, namely, heightened status and the approval of Mrs. Cosgrove. Other rewards were added as well, including extra time off the ward, special recreational opportunities, and the prospect of transfer to a ward that was closer to eventual discharge.

In describing the changes that Mrs. Cosgrove was able to bring about, we must mention the various ways she contributed to establishing a more homelike atmosphere. For example, the curtains at the windows and flowers in window boxes in the dining room, innovations which she initiated, made the surroundings more pleasant. Both the curtains and flowers were destroyed several times by patients, which was enough to discourage anybody. Each time, however, they were replaced, until the patients finally came to accept them as part of their environment. After a year and a half Mrs. Cosgrove added a canary bird and two love birds to the dining room, which is also used as a visiting room.

The birds and flowers are cared for by Mr. Kane, a schizophrenic patient with marked depressive behavior. Noting his frequent crying episodes and realizing how difficult it was to establish good rapport with him, Mrs. Cosgrove tried to find out what kind of work would interest him. By chance conversation she discovered that he had considerable knowledge of flowers and asked him to take charge of the window boxes. Gradually he became keeper of the birds as well. Finally, he was able to assume responsibilities in the kitchen. The crying spells have disappeared and occasionally one even finds him smiling as he cares for the birds or finds a new flower blooming.

Another improvement was in the form of a large bulletin board, which was placed to the left of the solarium entrance. Items of interest to the patients, cartoons, and pictures were placed there by means of scotch tape. These were supplied by the staff at first but this responsibility was gradually taken over by the patients, those who were able to help, alternating weekly in the job. Now even relatives and visitors have begun to bring in material.

Many of the results of the remotivation procedures on Ward J-4 have been apparent in our description of the habit training therapy and other activities. Two years after the program started and at the time the ward was visited in this Survey, Mrs. Cosgrove had decorative, homelike, and clean living quarters for her patients. Practically all of the patients were going through the routine without the assistance of ward personnel; restraints had been reduced almost to zero. The need for hydrotherapy had dropped from approximately 4,000 hours a month to 1,000. From the beginning of the second year of training about 35 patients were transferred to other wards for further rehabilitation. With an enviable record of this kind, it is not surprising to learn that Mrs. Cosgrove received the Psychiatric Aide Achievement Award in 1952. Furthermore, Ward J-4 has been designated the habit training clinic for the whole male section of the hospital, and a special training area for student aides.

COMMENTS AND CONCLUSIONS

Habit training is the "bread and butter" of remotivation, for it is the basic ingredient in changing apathy and discouragement by the staff to optimism. The back wards in any mental hospital, of which J-4 was typical in the beginning, are unpleasant and dismal places, constant reminders of the futility of therapeutic measures, and constant reinforcing agents for the Legend of Chronicity. Successful habit training is, therefore, the first step in reversing the pattern of discouragement.

A number of factors were important to the remotivation program on J-4, either contributing to the success of habit training or to further reawakening of dormant patient skills and interests. For example, the rules and order that are found on a Museum Ward were essential to a workable habit training routine. The level of patient adjustment was so poor that it was necessary to impose a regular and definite structure on ward events. The crucial difference between J-4 and the typical Museum Ward, however, was in the expectations toward patients. Mrs. Cosgrove and her staff firmly believed that the men could be helped; in this frame of reference the rules and order became aids to treatment rather than ends in themselves.

Development of occupational roles, a form of social classification, was another factor which should be noted. The status of Patient Helper, Clothesroom Man, and Symptom Spotter are all examples of the positive use of a social classification. Furthermore, the occupational roles were organized into graded levels of achievement, with rewards and prestige accruing to each level. The job classification rating, from A to D, offered visible evidence to the patients of therapeutic progress, not to mention the beneficial influence it had on staff attitudes. Mr. Orr, the former master painter, or Mr. Kane, who loved the birds, were examples of definite improvement.

A further point was the fact that the staff found out that patients got better by doing many different things. They told the observer that some got better by "sorting clothes, others by serving food, still others by scrubbing the shower and toilet. Then there were those who improved when they felt they had a stake in redoing the walls of the ward, or painting pictures, or making hooked rugs." In commenting on this observation, Miss Lane and Mrs. Cosgrove said, "All these activities are useful, we think, but there's got to be a purpose in all you do, and you have to do and be with patients and think with them, not just do things for them or leave them alone. Also, the patients have to see results, just like anybody else."

Our final comment is that the habit training program on J-4 utilized the existing resources of the hospital. It did not require the expenditure of extra funds, or the addition of new equipment. Within the realities of the everyday ward situation, using the furniture already there, getting along with limited toilet facilities, a successful program of social remotivation was put into operation. The crucial factor was the imagination and initiative of Mrs. Cosgrove, and the willing support given by her staff. The ingredients of imagination and initiative, factors in Mrs. Cosgrove's personality, had been sharpened and directed by the psychiatric aide class at Lynwood State Hospital. From beginning to end, the program on Ward J-4 was a result of the judicious rearrangement and utilization of staff and equipment, sparked by the belief that something could be done to help the chronic mental patient.

4. The House of Miracles

THE CHRONIC PATIENT who is also assaultive and abusive toward other patients or the staff is always a problem in mental hospitals. Constant supervision of him means that aides have less time to spend with other patients, time that might be profitable in starting these patients on the road to recovery. The use of various types of restraint, of hydrotherapy, and of wet packs has helped to control the difficult patient but it is not possible to keep him always in restraint or packs. Again, these procedures use an inordinate amount of personnel effort for a few patients.

With the advent of psychosurgery in the late 1930's, a partial solution for this problem appeared to be at hand. Although lobotomy was used on relatively few patients, and many were not helped by the operation, a considerable percentage of patients with severe obsessional states, agitated depressions, or severe chronic schizophrenia improved sufficiently after surgery for discharge or at least showed improved hospital adjustment. It was noted, however, that this improvement did not come about immediately after the operation. Retraining in such basic habits as feeding and elimination as well as social relations was necessary. Without such efforts the care of the lobotomized patient could well increase over that in his preoperative state. Retraining, however, requires time and people, precious commodities in any state hospital. It is no wonder, then, that lobotomy wards, or neurosurgical wards as they might be more correctly called, have often fallen short of their intended function, to the frustration of the staff and the detriment of the patient.

The Survey, however, found a number of heartening efforts in the direction of remotivating lobotomy patients. The observer noted that one kind of procedure appeared to work well in one

71

hospital, a different procedure to be characteristic of another hospital. Together they added up to a total program that might be utilized in any institution that had the resourcefulness to put it into practice. We are therefore presenting our story in three stages, as a composite picture, beginning with a program of basic retraining in a large western hospital. Then we move east to consider a plan of "side-room treatment" for those patients who appear to be least affected by retraining. Finally, we return to the West, to a small hospital that developed a helpful program of group discussions with relatives.

A LOBOTOMY RETRAINING WARD

One of the key hospitals in a large state system is the setting for the first aspect of lobotomy patient remotivation. Because of its large size, there were many chronic patients on its wards who were likely candidates for lobotomy; in addition, patients were transferred there from other hospitals for psychological evaluation and possible surgery. Care of the lobotomized patient, consequently, was an ever-present problem.

The impact of remotivation is most striking when considered against the background of the "old ward," the place where the neurosurgical patients were housed prior to the retraining project. The patients, all women, had been seriously ill, without even temporary remission, for about two years, and most had been patients for about five to seven years. The picture of the wards from which they had come was quite uniform, the patients continually confined to the ward, and thought too disturbed to be taken to the hospital dances. Even occupational therapy was not available. Occasionally one of them would try to sew, but other patients would interfere and nothing much resulted. Most of the movement on the ward was due to dependable and docile patient workers, the "occasional mood worker," and the "fringe workers." The patients who were noisy and disturbed tended to absorb most of the energy of the attendants. Others squatted around the walls, or lay scattered on the floor, often in the same place from one day to the next. From time to time one patient would attack another, or an attendant, for no apparent reason, and as quickly revert to inertness again. If approached and encouraged to do something, many would become obscene and nasty, one reason for staff reluctance to have much direct contact with them.

Staff Feelings About the Old Ward

Patients from wards similar to the "typical" ward just described were transferred to the lobotomy ward if the physician thought psychosurgery might be valuable. The lobotomy ward was not popular with the staff; in fact, there was difficulty in persuading nurses and aides to work there. A number of reasons lay behind this reluctance, not the least of which was that lobotomy was regarded as the end of the road, the last resort. To that extent the lobotomy patient represented a failure of medicine, and few people like to be associated with failure. Further, the patients were usually transferred to the ward two or three weeks before the operation, lobotomized, then remained on the ward for a period of a few weeks or months, after which they were returned to the ward or hospital from which they had come. This short period for contact with an individual patient precluded anything more than physical care or concern for her psychological needs of the moment. It proved to be essentially surgical nursing, not psychiatric nursing. The nurses and aides absorbed and magnified these feelings, and passed them on to the others, creating considerable dissatisfaction.

A New Retraining Ward

Realizing the dissatisfaction of staff and aware of the necessity for a program of retraining in addition to the surgery, the hospital established a special neurosurgical ward in July, 1951, where such a program might be carried out. The primary aim was the restoration of as many patients as possible to an adequate level of functioning so that they could leave the hospital. The secondary aim was a compromise and a practical objective, to enable the rest of the patients to reach a more satisfactory level of hospital adjustment in terms of being useful members of a ward and relatively happy with their lot.

The ward was located in a one-story building and had bed space for 60 patients. The division of the ward was not unusual, consisting of two 30-bed dormitories, a dining room, a dayroom that could accommodate all the patients at one time, a clothes-room, a pantry and ironing room, and two side rooms. A long wide corridor opened into the dormitories, the dayroom, and an enclosed patio-type yard. The furnishing of the ward was un-usual, for the furniture was new and comfortable. There were varicolored easy chairs, covered in plastic, mirrors on the wall, and many unscreened windows (those that faced the enclosed yard). Finally, the walls were freshly painted in pastel colors.

The staffing pattern for the ward was increased, so that the morning shift consisted of the supervisor, usually a nurse, three to four aides, two aide trainees, and one student nurse. The after-noon shift was usually in charge of the chief aide, with two or three aides and two aide trainees. The night shift consisted of two aides. It must be admitted at the outset that had the ward not been designated an aide training area the project would probably not have been possible.

Initiating the program presented difficulties. The head nurse and chief aide were pleased to be offered a position of responsi-bility in the venture but had never worked on a neurosurgical ward. Therefore, they accepted with some reluctance. Matters were not helped by the resentment of the veteran staff who had come from the previous lobotomy ward regime. These people gave the patients good physical care but often ignored or ridi-culed the suggestions of the head nurse or chief aide for in-corporating ideas of psychiatric nursing into neurosurgical nursing.

In spite of this stress a schedule was quickly established for the daily activities of the patients on the ward. This was varied from patient to patient in keeping with the nature of the population, some being oldtimers, others newly admitted patients, some most promising in adjustment, others much less so. The schedule emphasized retraining in basic areas like sphincter and bladder control, eating habits and table manners, in the use of hands and body in various skills, and in other areas like recreation, social

responsibility, and music. The general daily schedule is repro-
duced below:

5:45 a.m.   Patients awakened and dressed, specialed to bathroom.
6:30 a.m.   Tooth brush drill.
7:00 a.m.   Ward cleaning: floor polishing, dusting, tidying rooms,
    to   sorting laundry, taking care of trash. As patients im-
8:15 a.m.   prove they should be allowed to help with other work
            on the ward and in the cafeteria.
8:15 a.m.   Breakfast. Patients' eating habits and table manners
            should be watched and instructions given accordingly.
9:00 a.m.   Toilet drill.
9:15 a.m.   Occupational therapy. Patients capable of adapting
            themselves to any form of occupation are taken to the
            occupational therapy shop daily, except Saturday and
            Sunday. Here they can sew, crochet, embroider, weave,
            color with crayons or paint, work with clay and
            ceramics, etc. Tasks are selected in keeping with the
            progress and ability of the individual patient. Patients
            who are not able to leave the ward but can do some
            form of occupational therapy go to a side room in the
            ward where they are supervised by an aide.
10:00 a.m. Recreation. Those patients not capable of going to oc-
            cupational therapy play volley ball in the yard, or are
            taken for walks on the hospital grounds. Patients are
            taken outside, especially out of the ward and yard
            atmosphere, whenever possible. Also, patients who are
            able to do occupational therapy often participate in the
            recreation in order to prevent routinization of activities.
11:30 a.m. Toilet drill and preparation for lunch.
12:00 p.m. Lunch.
12:30 p.m. Toilet drill.
1:00 p.m.   Occupational therapy or choice of individual patient
            activities.
2:00 p.m.   Recreation. After the noon specialing for toilet drill the
            patients sit or stroll in the yard until prepared for vari-
            ous activities. For example, on Tuesday there are
            movies or TV, on Wednesday the rhythm band, games
            or marching, activities which are supervised by a music
            therapy program at the occupational therapy shop. On
            other afternoons patients are taken for long walks, play
            ball, or are entertained on the ward with music, sewing,
            reading, and games.

4:45 p.m.   Wash and prepare for supper.
5:15 p.m.   Supper.
5:45 p.m.   Toilet drill.
6:30 p.m.   Recreation, consisting of reading, games, and music, all
             of which are held outside when the weather permits.
8:15 p.m.   Preparation for bed.
9:00 p.m.   Lights out.

During the night the patients who had been operated on recently were taken to the toilet every two or three hours, until they stopped bedwetting; then, as often as necessary according to their individual needs.

"Paint and Powder" and Other Normal Activities

Patients were allowed to go to bed an hour later on Saturday night and get up an hour later on Sunday morning. The hope was that to a certain extent this would make life on the ward seem like life outside the hospital. This was met in other ways as well. On special occasions the nurses or aides would take selected patients to the circus or county fair, or relatives were encouraged to take patients on picnics or home for the weekend. The emphasis was on the utilization of any activities which were associated with normal living.

One interesting example of this emphasis was in the use of cosmetics. The ward staff felt that lipstick and powder were as important to the female patients as shaving was to the men, and began to bring in cosmetics for the patients. The head nurse on the ward was rather unhappy about this, for it was an expense to the staff which she felt they should not have to bear. Each ward received three dollars a month for incidentals for patient care but this could not be used for cosmetics since it was already budgeted for other purposes. Discussion with the superintendent of nursing service and eventually with the medical superintendent brought the decision that these articles could be purchased through the pharmacy. Thus, the application of powder and lipstick became a daily aspect of patient care. But now that the faces looked well cared for, the staff did not like the white stockinette caps that the postoperative patients wore. The answer to this was colorful scarfs, which were supplied by the staff, relatives, or friends. Bright cotton wash dresses and colored tennis shoes were ordered through the housekeeping department to complete the picture of good grooming.

One major difficulty remained. Although all the patients now looked presentable, a few of them could not be taken off the ward because of incontinence. In spite of the regular toilet-training drill there were still problems. For these patients, men's cotton shorts that were quite absorbent were secured. Now the head nurse was satisfied that her patients were as presentable as those from other wards. This was more than neurosurgical nursing; it was psychiatric nursing that all understood and in which they could see the results of their efforts. As a result, the whole ward population could be taken on walks and picnics, just like patients from other psychiatric wards.

Art, Rhythm, and Religion

Paintings and other results of the occupational therapy work on the ward were taped to the walls, but every time they were replaced the tape pulled the paint off. This ruined the walls and brought a decree from the medical director that nothing could be taped to any painted walls in the wards. Everyone wanted the work displayed but had to be content with the decision that projects could be taped only to the lower half of the corridor walls, which were tile. This seemed at best a poor substitute, for the projects would not be in the area where the patients spent most of their time. However, it turned out to be an improvement rather than a detriment, for now everyone who visited the ward passed the work and could comment on it.

These artistic endeavors were extended by painting murals on the windows at special holidays like Christmas and Easter. Display of the work by both staff and patients strengthened their bonds of understanding, gave the patients a feeling of pride, and increased the kind of social interaction that was so necessary for remotivation toward acceptance of normal social responsibility.

Other aspects of life outside the hospital were not neglected. One of these was religion. The second Monday and Tuesday of every month was scheduled for a visit by a Jewish rabbi. Every Wednesday a Bible class was conducted for Protestant patients and on Saturday evening confessions were held for Roman Catholics. Mass for Catholics was at 8:30 Sunday morning, followed by a Christian Science service twice a month at 1:00 p.m. and a Protestant service at 2:45. Patients who were able and were interested could join the choir, which practiced every Friday afternoon and sang at the Sunday services.

A few months after the retraining project was begun a physical therapist organized a percussion or rhythm band, in which both the patients and staff soon became active participants. It proved to be noteworthy because it was one activity that could engage the interest of all the patients on the ward, even those whose lobotomy was quite recent. Again, this was an activity that united both staff and patients in spirit as well as in active participation.

Part of one day each week, Saturday morning, was set aside for letter writing. In this, the aides helped and encouraged the patients to reestablish a vital link with other people, and especially with the outside world.

The "Family Room" Experience

The feature social occasion every week was afternoon tea, an event which must be seen in the wider context of an interesting technique in remotivation, which we have called the "family room" experience.

One of the side rooms on the ward had been designed for use as a nurse's station and was equipped with a 220 volt electrical line, hot and cold water outlets, and a drain which could be connected to a sink. It was not too difficult to make the room into a kitchen, then to add some small tables, captain's chairs, and a couch. Thus the side room became a family room, much like the old-fashioned kitchen around which at one time most of the social activities of the house revolved.

Those women who had improved sufficiently in their social skills were allowed the privileges of the family room and given the responsibility of preparing afternoon tea and also the refreshments for special ward parties or for social gatherings after an evening movie. With the assistance of the nurses or aides the patients went shopping for the supplies, then divided the tasks involved in food preparation and serving. Some were responsible for baking cookies and making fancy sandwiches, others for setting the tables, some for arranging flowers which had been brought in by the aides, and still others for "cleaning up" and washing the dishes. The ward staff were careful to make sure that these tasks rotated among the patients and that the washing of dishes did not always fall to the same women. Actually, the experience of preparing afternoon tea provided the opportunity for teaching valuable social skills, especially those related to the division of labor and the necessity of cooperation. Rotating the tasks gave each patient the chance to practice gradually the varied aspects of ordinary social living.

In time, the family room came to be utilized for other activities connected with food. Baking of cookies for afternoon tea had proved so successful that those patients who were able were encouraged to try their hand at baking pies and cakes. Baking contests were held, and at the time of the Survey visit some of the women proudly displayed to the observer the ribbons they had won for prize cakes. Some even felt it their duty to relieve the simplicity of hospital diet with their cooking and share their special apple pie with all the other patients on the ward. For them, the ultimate reward came through requests of other patients and staff for their recipes.

There were potential dangers in the operation of the family room, dangers of which fortunately the staff were aware from the beginning. Jealousy and complaints about two classes of citizens on the ward could disrupt harmonious relations among patients and possibly retard the remotivational process. However, it was made clear at all times that the privilege of being a "hostess" in the family room was open to all members of the ward, the only requirement being an improvement in personal habits and in the ability to make good social relationships with other patients. The fact was underscored when the women saw particular patients improve and immediately be accepted in the "hostess" status. Potential social stress and frustration was thus channeled into constructive ends, as seen in the remarks of the ward physician: "You can't have effort without some frustration and anger, the only problem is whether the energy is used in a constructive manner. Frustration is not bad for anyone; it only becomes so when it is associated with a feeling of helplessness or futility. We try to channel the patient's emotional energies by helping her, often despite herself."

Not only was the privilege of the family room held out as a reward for improved social behavior, but those who enjoyed its membership were not allowed to exploit their position in a socially destructive sense. Indeed, the staff impressed them with the fact that with added privilege goes added responsibility. Those women who were more advanced in social relations were led to understand that they had an obligation to assist those less advanced, and to help them in simple tasks that were a part of preparing for teatime or other social events. Furthermore, the staff made it clear that participation in the family room activities was not automatic or irrevocable, that responsibilities must be met regularly if privilege was to be continued.

Those activities in the family room that revolved around the preparation, serving, and consuming of food became the most successful of all ward activities in helping the disturbed and non-verbal patients again to pick up slowly the skill of conversation and social interaction. Since the food activities were usually in connection with an important occasion on the ward, there was an opportunity to linger and chat with ward friends, staff, and guests. The consuming of food was no longer merely a biological necessity but became a time of relaxation and conversation, a fulfillment of the symbolic values that our culture has long associated with eating. Evidence of the importance of these activities to all patients on the ward could be seen in changes in eating habits of the disturbed patients at regular mealtimes; no longer grabbing and gulping, or sitting mute and refusing, but slowly matching the pattern of those who had made greater progress toward finding their way back to normal social relations.

Evaluation: Changes in Patients and Staff

As vacancies due to transfers and discharges occurred during the next few years, newly lobotomized patients were admitted to the ward for remotivation and reintegration. When they improved sufficiently, they were transferred to open wards, or even directly to the community. The turnover was not rapid and there were discouraging failures but it was noted that once the program was in full swing, marked improvement could be seen in patients newly admitted. Successes were not so spectacular with those whose operations had taken place a year or more prior to their transfer to the retraining ward.

Partial evidence for the success of remotivation is found in the record of hydrotherapy and wet-pack treatments. When the schedule was first established, definite times were set aside each day for "hydro" and packs, a third of the patients needing this kind of treatment. As the program continued this need diminished. However, patients were transferred to the ward from time to time who did not belong there because of overcrowding on other wards. Furthermore, some of the most regressed patients required "hydro" or packs after even a year of continued effort. But the total number dwindled from the third that had existed at the beginning to a handful after the first year.

In trying to evaluate the effects of a retraining program one needs to look not only at the status of the patients but to learn something also about the feelings of the staff. The reader will remember that the old lobotomy ward was unpopular and the cause of numerous requests for staff transfers. On it there was a feeling of frustration and failure. This changed rather strikingly on the new ward as the retraining program became established; in fact, a common expression was that "It's a miracle what has happened to this place and to the patients." It seemed appropriate to us that the feeling on the part of the staff should be reflected in our chapter title; hence, "The House of Miracles."

THE "SIDE-ROOM TREATMENT"

Even miracles have a way of paling under certain circumstances. As we indicated above, there was a hard core of regressed patients that made little or no progress with the retraining program. They were a constant reminder that the effort had not been completely successful. Actually, the hospital had gone about as far as it could in working with the lobotomy patient; it had made a substantial emotional investment as well as one of personnel and time in the new retraining ward. The staff accomplished a great deal but were not able under the circumstances to take the next step, that is, to find a way of helping the regressed patient who seemed to resist all their efforts. Events in a hospital far to the east provided the material for this next step in our description of remotivation of lobotomy patients. In essence, the program we are about to describe represents an expansion and growth of an activity which was present in a more informal way in the first hospital.[1] This reflects no discredit on the first institution, for its contribution in general retraining is noteworthy; rather, the following account shows another facet of what is needed to make a total program.

"Intensive Social Reintegration Program"

The title of this section is the complete name of what was popularly called "side-room treatment."[2] It was a remotivation program tailored for a selected group of socially isolated lobotomy patients whose reaction to the general ward program was only sporadic or mechanical in nature. The plan was to bring together 10 to 12 patients, one nurse, and one aide in such circumstances that they could develop a close and enduring relationship for a period of not less than nine months. The hope was that through this personal and intensive association some of the most intractable lobotomy patients might come to achieve a better hospital adjustment. It also provided an excellent opportunity

---

[1] In the daily schedule, presented on page 75, the reader will note that under the activities at 9:15 a.m., patients who were not able to leave the ward but could do some form of occupational therapy, went to a side room on the ward where they were supervised by an aide.

[2] This particular project is very similar to one carried out at a hospital in Glasgow, Scotland. The reader is referred to: Cameron, J. H., R. D. Laing, and A. McGhie, "Patient and Nurse," *Lancet*, vol. 28, 1955, pp. 1384–1386.

to train nurses and aides on an inservice basis in interpersonal and occupational therapy skills.

The place selected for the special treatment program was one of the larger side rooms of the ward, off the main corridor. It was bright and well furnished and had a many-windowed view of the well-kept but busy hospital grounds. Also it contained magazines, knitting material, rags for making hooked rugs, reeds for baskets, and drawing, painting, and clay materials.

Treatment began at 9:30 in the morning, five days a week, continued to 11:30, began again at 1:30 p.m. and lasted until 4:30. Thus, the patients spent five of their waking hours in this fashion. The nurse and aide who carried the responsibility for the program shared general ward duties until 9:30, then later in the day wrote up their daily report between 4:30 and 5:00 p.m. In addition, they had weekly discussions with the medical staff and nursing education department. Fortunately, it was an honor to be selected for the task; otherwise, the heavy schedule might have made some reluctant to consider a position of this kind.

For the first few months the side-room staff expended most of their efforts on getting patients to do things, or preventing them from doing things, more often the latter. In their regressed state they clung to their meager possessions, simple things that they brought with them from the ward, or their positions in the room. Guarding their chairs was an intense preoccupation. Sometimes the anxiety and weariness of being in contact with these social isolates for such a length of time showed in the nurses' faces, or in their actions in sedating some of the patients who were overactive and thought of the side room merely as an extension of the ward.

As the months rolled by the patients and staff got to know each other better and to do things together. Actually, the first sign of improvement dated from the time that both the nurse and aide and the patients began to think that the other had changed. The improvement was first observable in the patients' personal habits and general appearance, then in improved relations with each other. Soon the patients began to do special little tasks of their own. Many of the types of activity that were conducted here were like those going on in the rest of the ward, but the occupational,

recreational, and physical therapists who visited the ward provided a source of professional advice that enabled the staff to
adapt activities to simple levels. Much of the work was in the
form of arts and crafts, making simple presents for friends or
relatives, knick-knacks for the ward, covers for the seats of chairs,
pulls for the blinds, mats for the tables. The patients worked as a
group, or at least this was so as time went on, and the staff were
careful to initiate activities that had a purpose or goal; the
articles were decorative but also useful. The room came to be
regarded as something special, something apart from the ward
routine, a place where you did things with people who felt the
same way as you did. To sum up, the emphasis was twofold, to
form close personal relationships among patients and between patients and staff, and to guide the patients into activities that were
useful and self-satisfying.

From time to time the patients in the side room would join the
rest of the ward at teatime; gradually as their esprit de corps
increased they began to have their own teas and invited other
patients from the ward to be their guests. This extension of the
self to others occurred somewhere between the sixth and eighth
months of the project and was the major sign that objectives were
being fulfilled. The room began to take on the appearance of a
sewing circle; that is, the patients came to be truly interested in
each other and helped each other in many small ways. The staff
now found the atmosphere there so comfortable that they ceased
to make notes about it in their daily reports.

Since the end of the minimum treatment period in the side
room had been reached, the clinical director felt that past efforts
were well worth the evident gains. Therefore, it was decided to
continue the program for an additional three months with the
hope of consolidating the gains. Plans for the next three months
were twofold; to use more complex activities like cooking or off-
ward recreation, and to start the process of weaning the patients
away from the close security of the side-room group. The staff
were ever mindful of the damaging effect of sudden changes on
these women who only recently had been in so regressed a
state.

The patients were overjoyed when they were permitted finally to use the simple cooking facilities that had been set up for the rest of the patients in the other side room. Further evidence of these passed-over patients becoming useful members of the hospital community came during the ninth and tenth months when some of them offered to help with ward chores, which they had consistently refused to do until this time.

Toward the end of the eleventh or twelfth month the patients were no longer social isolates and had begun to participate in some of the off-ward activities with other patients. Obscene, irrelevant, and stilted speech was largely replaced by more appropriate language. As verbal communication improved and the staff did not have to rely so heavily on the interpretation of gestures, interpersonal relations became warmer and more normal. It was evident that mutual barriers had been removed and that these patients could perform a variety of tasks formerly unimaginable.

It would be incorrect to imply that the project always ran smoothly and without problems. The reader can undoubtedly anticipate many of the things that were bound to happen. One of these problems was jealousy, a feeling by the patients in the side room that they were "special," and a feeling of envy on the part of the rest of the ward inhabitants. The answer to this was slow in coming, and only became obvious when it was learned that the side-room patients could become good general ward helpers; for example, they could, if willing, help in making beds. Furthermore, since the supplies and money for the side-room program were not handled separately from the general ward funds, the head nurse felt a certain amount of both administrative and emotional investment in the project. Eventually, ward staff members came to point with pride to their ward as the one that was selected for this special therapeutic effort and inservice training.

The staff probably learned as much as did the patients. As important as anything was the ability to anticipate felt needs of the patients, to be willing to take a chance on the ability of the patient to plan for himself. This came to replace the former concern with prohibition of unwanted or asocial activities. Direct intervention was slowly replaced by greater reliance on the patient and his own foresightful planning in terms of his perception of ward reality.

One of the older aides expressed her feelings about it as follows:

> I never thought I could get to like these patients, but I do like to be with them now. They look up to me and try hard when they know you like them. It doesn't matter what they try to do, it seems to me; they want your understanding and to know that you care more. Of course, you don't make them do difficult things at first, just go along with them easylike.

When the year was over a new special treatment group with two new staff trainees was formed. The results at the end of eight months with this new group were such that the administration decided the length of the program could be shortened to nine months, especially since the rest of the ward staff had become more skilled in the meantime and could absorb the new group of room-retrained patients without too much trouble.

A RELATIVES' ORIENTATION PROGRAM

If patients are to be remotivated for eventual discharge, the hospital cannot neglect preparing the relatives to receive them. This is an essential part of preparation of the environment, of equal importance with finding jobs and living quarters, and making financial arrangements. The remotivation program in the large state hospital with which we opened this chapter stressed work with the relatives of lobotomy patients as an important function in its retraining activities. The efforts of that hospital, however, were not developed to so high a degree as those of another western institution visited in the course of the Survey. We turn, then, to the latter institution for a description of the third aspect of remotivation for lobotomy patients, work with the relatives.

Relatives Feel Anxious and Inadequate

It was the common experience of nurses and aides on the lobotomy ward that relatives had many questions about the progress of patients. Many seemed genuinely interested in any improvement which might be brought about, but when it was suggested that they take the patient out for a few hours or home for overnight they were quite apprehensive. They had learned from previous occasions during the patient's hospitalization that they could not handle her when on visit. They were even more hesitant about assuming the responsibility of taking the patient home for an extended visit or on trial discharge. In addition to their fear of the patient the obvious personality changes, such as lack of initiative, motor and mental retardation, bedwetting, irresponsibility, lack of organization, and lack of interest were overwhelming. And, finally, the amount of supervision and instruction that the patient required after surgery created apprehension and feelings of inadequacy in the relatives, especially in regard to the duration of the need for this type of care.

Not only were these important factors in the postoperative adjustment of the patient, so was the time consumed in answering individual questions by the relatives and by giving support and assurance. The retraining program made heavy demands on staff time in itself; additional time for individual relatives was a definite strain.

Thus it was that in July of 1952 the head nurse and the assistant charge aide on the lobotomy ward proposed that one hour a week be scheduled for meeting with relatives. Initially, they planned to tell the relatives about the nursing problems they encountered on the ward and how they handled them, and to answer questions about the behavior of individual patients. They hoped that this would encourage relatives to take patients home for short visits and give them the courage to attempt more permanent arrangements. When this latter stage was reached, the group meeting could provide support and information for the problems encountered in the home.

Potential trouble lurked in a proposal of this kind. Both the medical staff and social workers might have good reason to feel threatened, the former because of the fear that the nurses might become overinvolved in emotional problems, the latter because work with relatives was their traditional domain. Besides, there was no hospital tradition of nurses doing group work, with either relatives or patients, which could be cited to strengthen their position. Awareness of these dangers had two effects on the nurse and aide who wished to start the meetings. In a positive direction, they were inclined to stress primarily the physical and nursing aspects of the care of the post-lobotomy patient. This meant concentration on patients' immediate problems. In a more negative way, they were hypersensitive to medical supervision of the meetings. They wanted to lead the meetings themselves, feeling they had the ability to do so, but were afraid that where it was not customary for nurses to lead groups they might lose the initiative to the medical staff. The qualms of both the nurses and the chief of service at this point in the development of the program were understandable. After some initial suspicion and heightened feelings, during which the continuous liaison by the nurse supervisor between the ward staff and chief of service did much to allay anxiety, confidence in the ability of the nurses was gained. Their hypersensitiveness turned to security and the relative orientation program settled into an accepted hospital practice.

Relatives Come to Meetings

Each new group member was given information on the patient's postoperative behavior, with emphasis on specific management problems which the staff had encountered. At this time the relatives could be helped to recognize that the patient's behavior should show definite changes after surgery, and the aims of the hospital for the patient could be clarified. As time approached for trial visit or discharge of the patient, attention was focused on the activities which might interest him when living at home, such as housework, gardening, movies, sightseeing tours, shopping, walking, and the like.

Participation by the relatives increased considerably once the patient left the hospital, for now they had everyday problems with which to deal. Presentation of these problems provided much material for the group to discuss, but the relatives also began to fulfill another group function at this point—support and assistance to other members of the group. The problems they had to present varied greatly, depending on the home situation and the difficulties in the patient's illness. Questions like the following were often heard: How do you get the patient up in the morning; how do you get her to bathe herself; how to get her into bed; how long to have her rest during the day; how to get her activated; how to develop interest in her appearance; how to get her to eat properly; how much to talk to the patient about her illness and surgery; what activities can she take part in; how to cope with the patient's hostility, tactlessness, and foolish and irresponsible behavior; and how to get her to socialize on a more acceptable level? Questions of this kind could not be asked apart from feelings about the behavior of the patient. Responses which the relative had made to various actions of the patient were brought out and discussed. Frequently other relatives had suggestions to make but they were most helpful to the questioning relative when they described how they had encountered similar difficulties. This often proved to be fully as reassuring as the support of the hospital staff.

In most patient-relative situations a critical point was reached when the patient began to assume more responsibility for her behavior and the relatives to decrease their supervision. One result was an expression of resentment by the patient that the relatives went to the hospital, while the patient herself was not being seen. In some cases it even resulted in a refusal by the patient to respond further to supervision by the relative. A hopeful sign, this critical point was met by the nurses' scheduling time for the patient when they could give ideas and suggestions for activities directly to her as a responsible adult. What might have been a slump or leveling off in the patient's progression toward better social adjustment was thereby often turned into positive effort in the achievement of responsibility.

Consequences of Relatives' Orientation

When the observer visited the hospital in 1954, the orientation program had been in operation for two years. In that period the relatives of 24 patients had been members of the group, the length of time they attended varying from one to ten months, depending on the condition of the patient and the needs of the relative. Of the 24 patient-relative situations, 18 lobotomy patients had been able to remain at home and make a satisfactory social adjustment. Eight of these were working and contributing to the economic needs of the family, while the other ten were helping with the housework under a minimum of supervision.

The conclusion drawn by the nurses and rest of the hospital staff is that when relatives can be reached and assisted they are more willing to approach the problem of home care for the patient. Furthermore, by the use of group meetings a greater number of relatives can be reached, with the result that a greater number of patients can be retrained for useful membership in society.

A CASE STUDY

Many of the points which have been made in this chapter are brought out in the following case presentation. The situation leading to lobotomy, difficulties following operation, results of retraining on the ward, vicissitudes at home when discharged, all these are evident in the case of Mrs. Doran, as she will be designated.

She was a forty-two-year-old white woman with a college education and some experience as a saleswoman and as a piano teacher. During her childhood she was a passive, submissive individual who never went out on dates or had much social life. Following graduation from high school she demanded to go away to college, where she met and later married a music teacher. She had one child, a boy, by this marriage. After thirteen years she divorced her husband, only to remarry him a short time later. Within six months she was mentally ill and was hospitalized in 1944. At this time she expressed paranoid ideas about people reading her mind, poisoning her, and so on. For the next eight years she was in and out of the hospital, receiving during this period four courses of electric shock treatment and a course of 56 insulin comas. Improvement was at the best transient and in July, 1952, she was again admitted to the hospital for evaluation and possible lobotomy.

On admission, Mrs. Doran appeared to be a neat, well-groomed woman with flattened affect, withdrawn, and showing reduced motor activity. She spent her time sitting, staring into space or out the window. She showed some ritual mannerisms in eating and walking and expressed the feeling that everything going on in her environment was done deliberately to annoy her. Only with urging would she participate in any ward activities, and then with a bored and tolerant expression on her face.

Two months later Mrs. Doran underwent lobotomy. At first, she was extremely slow in all her activities, requiring spoon-feeding for the first week, and supervision in other activities such as dressing, elimination, and the general ward routine. She was started immediately on the retraining program, being urged to feed herself and to tend to her own toilet needs. Soon she was eating by herself and in about ten days she would go to the toilet without being reminded. However, she would sit on the toilet for long periods, so that it became necessary on many occasions to force her to get up. She was urged to join the many ward activities, like the rhythm band and the occupational therapy classes, and to come to the weekly afternoon tea. The staff prodded her to make more decisions on her own. There was gradual improvement in the acceptance of responsibility and the carrying out of decisions, but supervision was still necessary.

She was sarcastic and insolent in her behavior, would keep her eyes closed, and dance about the hallway laughing in an inappropriate manner when not participating in organized or supervised activities.

Five weeks following lobotomy, the staff decided that the patient had improved sufficiently for a trial home visit. Inasmuch as her husband had by now divorced her a second time, the mother was the only available relative with whom she could live. It was the consensus that this arrangement should be tried in spite of the known hostility between the two. Apprehensive to the point of being overwhelmed by what she would do with Mrs. Doran at home, the mother was invited to join the relatives' orientation group.

Mrs. Doran's mother was relieved at this suggestion and eager to join the group. She first met with the others when she began taking her daughter out on an occasional pass. At this time the general problems encountered with all postoperative patients were reviewed with her, also problems encountered with Mrs. Doran in particular and modes of handling them were discussed. The nurses told her of the patient's slowness in dressing, her reluctance to get off the toilet, and especially her facetiousness and sarcasm.

Mrs. Doran was then discharged to her mother's supervision, with the group meetings to be continued every week. There were many problems. The daughter would not get up in the morning, would not take a bath, or if she did, would refuse to get out of the tub. She refused to dress properly and resisted being activated in any manner. Bodily assistance was often necessary, to which she retaliated with assaultiveness, so that on many occasions it became necessary to call for outside help.

Hostility toward her mother reached the point at the end of two months that Mrs. Doran would refuse to do anything that her mother suggested, would not talk to her except to criticize or nag, and refused to call her "mother." It is hardly surprising that the mother became anxious and upset, trying to push her daughter harder and harder but getting fewer results. At this point it was suggested that the nurses see the patient in order that suggestions for behavior would come from a third person, thereby lessening the tension between the two women. Mrs. Doran came to the hospital for a half-hour conference each week just before the group meeting. She was most appreciative of the interest and responded readily to suggestions made by the nurses. Each week under the nurses' supervision she prepared a written schedule of activities, which helped to motivate her and get her back into social activities. The following week she would report on the results, and the reasons she did not accomplish certain things were discussed. Her mother was kept informed of these events but asked not to become involved in pushing the patient, but rather to be available as needed. This procedure was continued for several months, during which Mrs. Doran learned greater independence but relied less and less on her written schedules. The prevailing attitude on the part of the hospital was that she was capable of being self-sufficient and expected to be so.

The overt hostility toward her mother gradually diminished, and six months after surgery it was decided that they could be on their own to a greater extent. They moved to a small town which both of them liked but they kept in touch with the hospital staff by mail and visits every two or three months. Mrs. Doran took the initiative in caring for her own appearance, volunteered to serve on the civil defense air watch, took up work in her spare time as a Gray Lady, and attended classes for self-improvement. She again found employment as a saleswoman and helped her mother with housekeeping, preparation of meals, and shopping. Her mother now feels relaxed with her and a mutually acceptable relationship has been established.

COMMENTS AND CONCLUSIONS

The Museum Ward is a far cry from the situations which we have described here but it would not be difficult for the post-lobotomy patient to fit into the pattern of a Museum Ward. The degree of regression, of unpredictable assaultiveness, of verbal sarcasm and hate which characterized the "old lobotomy ward" in the first hospital is sufficient to make many hospital personnel feel that only repressive measures will bring control. In the early stages of postoperative behavior, transfer to a Museum Ward might well appear to be a reasonable solution.

Furthermore, the retraining program could have turned into a Moving Ward situation. Although many of the patients were not able to leave the ward, the pressure of activity could have become an end in itself, the schedule of events a rigid taskmaster.

That neither of these events occurred in our situations was due to many factors, but here we would like to emphasize only a few. In the first place, the staff were willing to make an investment in the patients as people. On the ward the staff and patients played, planned, and worked as a unit. The patients felt that their efforts were wanted, that their contribution helped the whole ward. Yet the work as a unit did not preclude the setting of individual goals for each patient, assigning activities that were in keeping with the level of adjustment, pushing gently but not shoving. The individual was not lost in the group effort but felt singled out and, therefore, important.

In time the staff in all three of the situations came to realize that the means or activities were not so important as the interpersonal relationships between nurse or aide and patient. The best examples of this are the "family room" experience and the "side-room treatment" where the activities were identical with those on the rest of the ward, yet the social relations were much closer and more intense. We could do no better here than repeat part of a statement of one of the aides in this program: "It doesn't matter what they try to do, it seems to me; they want your understanding and to know that you care more."

The place of food in the remotivation of mental patients, as shown in the "family room" experience, is most significant. Too often hospital personnel have not understood, or have neglected, the symbolic importance of food in daily life. Many of our early emotional relationships have a close association with eating, and later experiences frequently reinforce the connection between eating and strength of ties to other people. In this framework, food signifies companionship, security, and closeness to those we love. All activities concerned with food, including preparation as well as actual consumption, therefore provide an opportunity to reawaken and reinforce feelings of security and mutual dependence.

Finally, it was apparent in the remotivation of lobotomy patients that one improvement created a situation that called for further improvements. To put it another way, the introduction of something new changed people's perception of the situation, revealing aspects of the patients that had not been seen before. After lipstick and powder were in general use, the stockinette caps were out of keeping with attractive faces. When scarfs were introduced, the hospital uniforms were out of keeping with the color and good grooming of the head. So it went. Remotivation in this case seemed to carry within it a certain power to keep itself going, power that would be utilized and strengthened as it met with staff interest and courage.

With the spreading use of tranquilizing drugs, psychosurgery is becoming much less frequent as a treatment of choice. That does not mean that the material presented in this chapter loses in value. The remotivation techniques described, especially the "family room" experience and the "side-room treatment," have applicability far beyond a lobotomy ward. There are still many patients who are assaultive and abusive, and there are many who respond poorly to the tranquilizers. Furthermore, there is growing evidence that if the use of drugs is to be maximally effective, it must be accompanied by psychological and social reintegration. In this light, activities on the House of Miracles are most relevant to problems in all state hospitals.

5. A Family of Elders

THERE IS A HARD CORE OF PATIENTS in mental hospitals who have resided there for years, some as long as forty years, some even longer. These patients by and large are now into old age, the normal problems of aging complicated by the long history of mental disturbance and the effects of continuous hospital existence. To this hard core of old folk must be added those over sixty who are being admitted to the mental hospital for the first time, a group whose numbers are steadily increasing. Therefore, it seems likely that among other things state hospitals must plan in the future on a greater number of wards for the care of old-age patients and must adapt their treatment techniques to the special problems of this population.

Treatment of the older patient, especially remotivation treatment, has its difficulties. In addition to the effects of deterioration in the central nervous system must be added the attitudes toward old age on the part of hospital personnel, attitudes that so easily reinforce the Legend of Chronicity. Even when a young patient is labeled chronic, a shred of hope lingers in the minds of ward staff, but when this label is given to an old patient the end of the road seems truly to have arrived. The Legend of Chronicity is reinforced because of the negative attitudes toward old age that are to be expected in a society that emphasizes youth. We tend to regard the retirement years as relatively useless, a time for "being put out to pasture." Young families often resent taking grandparents into their home, feeling that they will be in the way or that they do not share the modern ideas in regard to rearing children. A devaluation of old age as a general cultural fact will be reflected in the devaluation of aging mental patients, a frame of reference which has a natural affinity for the Legend of

Chronicity. The treatment of the senile patient may therefore be one of the most unrewarding jobs in the hospital.

In spite of these difficulties the Survey found some impressive examples of ward situations where the fears and anxieties of old age were being allayed and the patients encouraged to reestablish worthwhile social relationships. The situation which we are about to describe was not the only one that came to the observer's attention, and, indeed, there have been other reports about successful geriatric wards.[1] However, this particular example seemed to illustrate rather well the principles of remotivation that we are emphasizing in this book.

THE WARD

The following account concerns a men's ward in a large state hospital in the Midwest where all but five of the 110 patients were over sixty-five years of age, and the oldest was ninety-five. Almost the full scope of diagnostic categories could be seen, although the proportions of each were rather different from the ward situations described in other chapters. Schizophrenia constituted about 8 per cent of the total, mainly "washed out" patients who had been in the hospital for many years. The largest group by far, some 40 per cent, was made up of patients with paranoid behavior, suffering from delusions and auditory hallucinations, a cantankerous lot and readily incited to anger. A quarter of the patients were depressed, disoriented as to time and place, but having a relatively good prognosis. Many of them were still hospitalized because there was no place for them in the community or they could not get along with relatives. Five or 6 per cent were classified as manic, were well preserved in appearance, and could get along with an occasional electric shock treatment to control their mischievous aggression and fright. Dementia characterized a similar number of the men, the "happy wanderers," as they were called, who would wander restlessly, accompany other patients on refuse and paper collecting details, and "get in the hair" of the stronger paranoid pa-

[1] Linden, M. E., "The Miracle in Building #53," *Currents*, January, 1954 (Pennsylvania Citizens Association, Philadelphia).

tients. Most of those with senile dementia were incontinent, some could appreciate the call of nature but not the proper place for it, using a shoe or tub or anything that was handy. Many were "strippers," taking their clothes off at every opportunity in much the same fashion as a two-year old child. There were also a few patients with epilepsy who showed little deterioration and got along well on dilantin, some who were mentally defective but were good workers, and an occasional one who was paretic.

Physical disabilities were in keeping with the expectations for this age group, showing such things as edema of the legs and restriction of joint movement. A few of them had difficulty with their balance and would fall unexpectedly, although these falls were not so frequent as they would have been on a ward with stairs. A few patients were bedfast or chair-ridden, some got around in wheel-chairs or tottered, but three-quarters of them were completely ambulatory. There was some indication that the number of ambulatory patients depended on hospital policy, for a few years ago, previous to the remotivation program, almost all the patients were bed- or chair-ridden, or on the verge of it. Two-thirds of the patients had normal sight and hearing for their age, the rest had loss that ranged from mild to severe. Only a few were blind or very deaf.

One of the main problems on a senile ward is incontinence but in this particular case some of the features of the remotivation program had reduced it to a minor irritation. One patient had both urinary and fecal incontinence without warning; one showed only occasional "errors" if there was sufficient staff anticipation; two had fecal incontinence alone; and four were "bedwetters."

Another aspect of the description of the patient population is a behavioral one, the activities of which the men were capable and the kinds of conduct they showed. Many were able to take care of all their needs, including the ability to shave themselves. About 25 per cent required some help in general tidying up, a smaller percentage needed attention from the staff in washing and dressing, while only 10 per cent required total attention. A third of the patients were in good contact and most of the total group were cooperative and nontroublesome. Of the rest, some were noisy, a fair number could be expected to show occasional aggression, some wandered and disturbed other patients, but only a very few resisted the ministrations of the nurses or aides. The troublesome patients were usually controlled by the cooperative ones, so that a kind of communal discipline existed.

Ward Environment and Geography

Most mental hospital wards are alike in their physical layout, having dormitories, dayroom, dining room, and side rooms; accordingly, one looks for exceptions in the physical environment in other aspects of the living space. Arrangement of the furniture, decorations, additions to the recreational and occupational equipment can make considerable difference in the atmosphere when compared to the traditional ward situation. These features were distinguishing characteristics of the ward under discussion when it was visited in the summer of 1954.

Furniture on the ward reflected a compromise between hope and financial reality; that is, there were functional easy chairs and tables in addition to the wooden rockers and benches. On the wall were Currier and Ives prints, railway posters, and calendar pictures of hunting and fishing scenes. These had been glued to the wall, then varnished, which meant that they could be washed easily but there was no danger of their falling and breaking. At one time there were flower vases attached to the wall, placed just out of reach of the patients. The success of this idea had led to the use of flower boxes on individual window sills, and widespread fear that the flowers would be picked, hoarded, and eaten was not substantiated to any noticeable degree. After that, metal vases were used for the mantels and tables without mishap. There were mirrors in numerous places, the corridors, dayroom, and dormitories. Said one of the aides, "Mirrors help keep patients tidy and even the shortest patients can look at themselves because we have all sizes. Of course, they're more important for women, but men need them too."

For the more alert patients who used books and writing materials, there were cabinet-type lockers in the hallway. When space permitted, there were bedside tables for the personal possessions of patients, because it was found that some of them could assume the responsibility of caring for their toilet articles, and thus needed less supervision.

The surroundings seemed very fitting for the chronic elderly patient. The dining room, for example, was the personal pride of all the patients; it was painted in cheerful colors and had attractive wall hangings, a whatnot in the corner, and pretty checked tablecloths. It was a cheerful place for eating as well as a pleasant room to entertain visitors.

Pride in the ward in general was fostered by allowing the more able patients to have certain privileges in planning and decorating their own work area. The Clothesroom Man, who was responsible for the orderly appearance of that room, was allowed to paint "his" furniture and keep the place as he liked it. The Linen-Room Man was good at repairing and painting, so that in addition to his linen-room duties he was encouraged to fix up his area according to a plan he worked out.

Pride was fostered in another way, too; by encouraging the patients to wear their own clothing and to be neat. The relation between good grooming and self-respect was emphasized; consequently, when visitors came to the ward a patient would often call attention to a new tie or some other special article of clothing he happened to be wearing. The obvious pleasure of the visitor or relative at this turn of events only served to boost morale a bit higher.

To conclude this section of orientation for the reader concerning the patients and the ward environment, a word should be said about geography, in the terms outlined in the first two chapters. It will be recalled that arrangement of furniture often coincides with informal divisions of the patients by certain social or behavioral characteristics. In this ward the dayroom area appeared to be divided according to the loss of time sense. Patients who were least in contact with reality and interested mainly in mealtime, could be found sitting close to the wall by the dining-room entrance. Their chairs were turned away from people toward the windows. Patients who were more alert, more attuned to the time schedule of ward events, could be found in chairs facing the ward office and entrance to the hallway, or gathered around the long tables in the solarium. Figuratively speaking, these two groups were worlds apart and illustrated some of the difficulties in remotivation that changes in ward environment alone could not overcome. This provides an appropriate place, then, for us to turn to the details of the remotivation program in its various aspects.

THE REMOTIVATION PROGRAM

Success with the retraining program on the habit training ward, which was described in Chapter 3, depended in no small measure on the personality and interest of the charge aide, Mrs. Cosgrove. Similarly, the remotivation on the ward for aged patients depended a great deal on the warm human interest shown by the charge aide, Mrs. Harlan. A brief sketch of her background is pertinent here because of certain similarities it shows with that of Mrs. Cosgrove, as well as the relevance of her background to her skills with patients.

Mrs. Harlan is now in her fifties, a Baptist minister's daughter, a former school teacher, and a pianist with a number of years of study in music. She has taught country grade school and also been a teacher of piano. Married in her early twenties, she spent some sixteen years as a farmer's wife before both she and her husband decided to work at the state hospital as attendants. While living on the farm she was active in church work and Women's Club activities as well as indulging in her chief hobby, horticulture. This she has developed to the extent that she collects bulbs and plants from all parts of the United States, and work in her flower garden is a means of relaxation after a busy and difficult day. After working in the hospital for a number of years she attended the hospital's class for psychiatric aides, and two years later she received the Psychiatric Aide Achievement Award of the year. Shortly after her graduation from the psychiatric aide class she was put in charge of one of the old age wards, a place which we have called the Family of Elders.

When the ward was visited in 1954 as part of the Survey, the remotivation of the aging patients was well established. Success of the program was due to a number of factors, not the least of which was the ability of the charge aide, Mrs. Harlan, to give personal attention to her hundred-odd patients, to treat them as individuals in need of care. She knew every patient by name, and knew something about his problems and his assets, and she used this knowledge in her work. Whenever a newcomer arrived on the ward she made sure that he was introduced to a number of the other patients, that he knew where to hang his coat and hat, where he could find the daily papers and other reading material, and that he had cigarettes or pipe tobacco. Her greeting was always the same: "We're happy to have you join our big family."

Her emphasis on individual attention to patients appeared in another way, in helping the patient who was upset over some happening during the day, or over a letter from home, or some slight that he may have received from another patient. These incidents were as important to her as the disturbance of an agitated patient who may do physical injury to himself or others. When one of her patients was upset, her procedure was to take him by the arm, walk around the ward with him; or if she had an errand to do, take the patient along with her. For those who were too infirm to walk she would take time to talk and to listen, especially to listen, for she realized how important it was to the aged men in her care to have someone they could depend on and who would listen to their troubles.

Mrs. Harlan's personalized care extended into other activities as well. Knowing the importance of personal appearance to her patients on special occasions, she would be careful to see that their clothes were in shape and their hair trimmed at these times. It is interesting that the barber shop, in an adjoining building, had proportionately more patients from her ward than from any other ward. She enjoyed dressing her patients in their Sunday best and sending them off to church. When a patient was ready for discharge she would wash his shirts, press his trousers, and pack his belongings, even though such service was not required of her. "Just like my old mother used to do," one of the patients said.

Perhaps this personal interest in each patient is the reason they all called her "Mom," even though many of them were old enough to be her father, and some could even pass for her grandfather. Remembering the worth of each person apparently helped her avoid becoming hardened to the suffering that she saw each day.

There are other qualities, closely related to that of personal interest, that contributed to Mrs. Harlan's ability to build an emotional atmosphere like that in a family. One of these is that she was a good observer, aware of subtle changes in behavior that indicate improvement, of the necessity for some change in a patient's routine to reduce anxiety. Often she would get in touch with the social service department when a particular patient showed signs of sufficient rapport to be placed in a boarding situation outside the hospital, or even return home. It is important to note in this connection that, although she was always eager to see her patients get well, she was saddened by their departure and the ending of a pleasant friendship.

Then there was the ability to draw patients into any activity that might be taking place on the ward. This did not always come easily and she would often have to spend considerable time in order to develop the interest of a patient in some job. Perhaps the most important part of drawing out patients was her persistence, for she refused to give up on the arousing of interest until the patient was taking part in activities with the rest of the men.

Mrs. Harlan's skill as a pianist stood her in good stead when the patients as a group became upset or disturbed, especially when there was a thunderstorm or high wind. Events of this kind are always disturbing to mental patients, making them fearful and restless, but in the Family of Elders music and group singing proved to be calming agents. Of course, the piano playing was important at other times as well, for parties and for general ward recreation, bringing the patients out of withdrawal and fostering the feeling of membership in a kin group.

These remarks sound much like a testimonial, and indeed they are in many ways. However, our observation has been that the remotivation of patients depends on the personal qualities of those who care for patients, not the least of which is the ability to regard each patient as important and useful. Mrs. Harlan exhibited this to a unique degree and in her relations with staff and visitors this comment was often made: "The remarkable thing about Mrs. Harlan is her ability to establish rapport with anyone she deals with."

Family Activities

There were celebrations on every legal holiday and a party for each patient on his birthday, which is no mean task when one remembers that the ward had a population of more than 100 and that there are at least a half-dozen major holidays during the year. Extra work was entailed but the obvious enjoyment shown by both patients and visitors made it worthwhile. Bingo was also an excuse for an occasional party for those patients who had the intelligence and were in sufficient contact with reality to play the game.

Once a week the hospital band came to the ward, an event eagerly awaited by everyone. Some brought out their own instruments to play along with the band, others sang and tapped their feet, many just listened. It was a surprise, but a pleasant one, to see a mentally and physically handicapped man shaking his rattle or simple toy instrument in time to the music, and to see his facial expression change from blankness to enjoyment.

The homelike atmosphere on the ward, the big family that Mrs. Harlan described to newcomers, was further enhanced by the fact that the regular and occasional ward help (some 40 of the patients) ate "home style" in the dining room. Food was served in big dishes and on platters from which each patient helped himself, and passed on to his neighbor. The other patients had tray service at the table, but could look forward to the day when they were sufficiently improved to join the "boarding house gang." Only the incontinent patients ate in a corner of the room under supervision. On Sundays and holidays, or at the birthday parties, the bright checked tablecloths were used.

Movies came to the ward every other week and four times a year there was a party and record hop on the ward to which women patients from other wards were invited. In addition, eight or ten of the patients regularly went to the general hospital dances in the auditorium, which were held each week.

Work Is Also Necessary

Practically all large state hospitals depend on patient help for a certain amount of the housekeeping activities on the wards. The Family of Elders was no exception, but it went one important step farther and made the men feel that the work they did was an important contribution toward the well-being of everyone on the ward. Patient work then came to have therapeutic value in itself, in addition to its importance for the regular maintenance of the ward.

Of the 110 patients, 20 or 25 could be regarded as regular ward help. Mrs. Harlan was heard to remark concerning regular ward helpers: "If conditions were favorable and people were more understanding of old people, about 10 patients would be just as satisfactory workers as those found outside; they are privileged patients."

In addition, another 25 of the men were classified as occasional ward help. Again, in the words of Mrs. Harlan: "They will do errands for me and small jobs. My philosophy is that six senile men can do the job of one healthy man, so I don't need any outside help to run the place."

From the regular and occasional ward workers roles were assigned that are reminiscent of those described on the habit training ward. There were Patient Bathers, Bed Makers, Patient Dressers, and Feeders. One was designated the Solarium Mopper, another the Pantry Man. Much of the success of the "home style" arrangement at mealtime was due to the willingness of the Pantry Man to wash the extra dishes that resulted, the platters, serving bowls, and side dishes. The Table Washer was very proud of his simple task; the Clothesroom Man, to whom we referred earlier, gloried in his place of work, not only because he could fix it up as he chose but also because it made a real contribution to ward morale.

The staff were careful to assign work roles on the ability of the individual patient to carry out the tasks involved, careful not to make the job a chore, and to advance the worker to a more responsible position when he gave evidence of improved adjustment. They also made sure that the work roles had prestige, and that patients received the rewards that go with high status positions, that is, praise and appreciation.

For the patients who were not able to handle regular work assignments, there was the "work party," an interesting institution in itself. Groups of patients would sit around a long table and shell peas, or snip beans, or make paper decorations for themselves or other wards. Usually, there was soda pop for refreshment sometime during the work, provided out of Mrs. Harlan's own purse or from a special patient fund, for Mrs. Harlan would say, half jokingly, half seriously, "When men work, they get thirsty."

These "work parties" seem particularly sensible for two reasons. In the first place, old people in mental hospitals are social rejects not only because they are mentally ill but also because, like many old people outside the hospital, they are not capable of doing a day's work. Again, this is part of the negative attitudes toward the elderly which are to be found in contemporary American culture. Working together on useful tasks tended to contradict this idea, and the beneficial effects were further enhanced when the work could be done in a party atmosphere. Second, much of the work was in connection with food, food that would be used on the ward. As we have indicated elsewhere in the book, food activities have important symbolic significance, and in the Family of Elders the work strengthened the feeling of kinship as well as reduced complaints about meals.

Another feature of the ward routine should be mentioned, even though its presentation here involves a shift in subject. A unique feature of old-age wards, in contrast to wards with younger patients, is that there is deterioration in body as well as mind. Thus, there are usually a number of frail patients. This poses problems of management and remotivation that are difficult, to say the least. In the Family of Elders the fit patients arose at six a.m. but the frail patients remained in bed until 9:30. It was during the hours just after the patients got up that many of the conduct problems appeared. Then the frail patients were most unsteady, confusion was maximal, and the paranoid and depressed patients were most difficult. One might also say that it was in these hours that the patience of the staff was most severely tried.

There is one final comment about ward routine. We mentioned earlier that the problem of incontinence had been much reduced in the course of the remotivation program. Success in toilet training depended, as on the Habit Training Ward and the House of Miracles, on a regular schedule for the patients who were known to be incontinent. Five times each day and three times each night they were taken to the toilet, a time-consuming procedure, but one that worked.

"The Sick Help the Sicker"

Patients can help in remotivation by helping each other. Mrs. Harlan had noticed that it was fairly typical for her oldsters to form friendship pairs, patterns that were very much like those on the outside, based on contiguity or shared interests of some kind. She also noticed that some of these pairs had developed in a leader-follower basis, that an infirm patient was regularly guided to bed by a stronger man. Accordingly, she capitalized on her observation and fostered whenever possible the association of patients for help or recreation.

It was not particularly difficult to arouse the interest of one patient in another, for they were all in the same straits and realized that they would have to make the best of it. Aiding each other helped to reduce their feeling of being worthless; assisting a patient to remain continent or to keep his clothes on raised the dignity of both the helper and the helped.

At one time the aides discouraged patients from getting together to chat or help each other, for they were afraid something would happen. It was also thought that the better patients, those who were quiet, kept their clothes on, and sat in the right places, should not associate with more regressed patients, for it would only cause trouble. Experience proved these ideas to be untrue. Mrs. Harlan's comment was: "Sometimes you can get the nicest people from patients that were in real bad shape if you give them a chance and maybe let other patients have a crack at them and help them out."

So it was that under the plan known as "The Sick Help the Sicker" nearly half of the men came to help each other. There were three blind men who were regularly guided to the toilet and to the dining room by other men who seemed to be their friends, all without any prompting by staff members. By being allowed to help each other the patients had a greater sense of freedom as well as of responsibility, of having worth rather than being worthless.

Two case illustrations from the ward situation will indicate some effects of the "sick helping the sicker."

One was that of an irritable arteriosclerotic patient, formerly a businessman, who was seventy-six years old and had been in the hospital for three years. He was classed as a constant complainer, claiming that the attendants or other patients stole his clothes and made him dirty. Unfortunately, his spinster daughter believed his fantastic tales and not only supported him but also complained to the doctors. The cranky behavior continued unabated and finally the patient began striking attendants with his cane.

At this point one of the other patients suffered a cardiac breakdown. He was some ten years younger, had been a good "mixer" on the ward, and had ground-parole privileges. As he convalesced from his illness he refused to leave his bed, even though digitalis was effective in controlling his condition, and became hypochondriacal. His bed was next to that of the irritable patient and during this period the two men found they had common interests and became fast friends.

The first patient, the one with the arteriosclerotic condition, chided and coaxed his friend until he got out of bed and the two would talk by the hour. The friendship produced a change in both of them, with the result that they even offered to perform minor ward duties, activities formerly disdained as beneath their station.

The second case concerned a seventy-year-old senile man who had been hospitalized for a year prior to his transfer to the Family of Elders. From a behavioral point of view he was a difficult patient. He had delusions and hallucinations, was confused and disoriented, noisy and restless. He refused to walk but could be induced to sit in a wheel-chair.

Shortly after his transfer he was sitting next to a fifty-year-old epileptic patient one day when the latter pitched forward from his chair in a seizure. The older man showed considerable interest in his neighbor's misfortune, and on being asked to help, got out of his wheel-chair and kept other patients away. The two became friends and the older man began to walk again and showed less difficulty with his speech. He took it upon himself to assist the epileptic to the toilet at regular times. Also, he began to show an interest in helping a mentally retarded boy who had been temporarily transferred to the ward because of overcrowding in other parts of the hospital.

Projects and Planning

Remotivation programs can be hampered by the fact that the staff who are most interested in the effort and instrumental in its success are concentrated in the morning shift. It was a happy fact that in the Family of Elders the charge aide who was responsible for the afternoon and evening shift was not only able but also imbued with the point of view of remotivation. Like Mrs. Harlan, she was interested in the patients as individuals and saw work or projects as means to better adjustment rather than as ways of keeping the patients busy or out of trouble. Furthermore, she had an advantage in being on the p.m. shift, for less time was needed to perform the service or housekeeping chores, and more time could be spent on recreational projects. Some of these seem worth describing.

The "tire-doll project" utilized old inner tubes which were supplied to the hospital by a local tire store. These the patients cut up and fashioned into baby dolls, which then were distributed to crippled children.

There was also a scrapbook project, in which patients cut pictures and cartoons out of magazines and pasted them into books. Many of the results were far from professional, but when sent to the local children's home or children's hospital they provided hours of enjoyment, not to mention the satisfaction the old men gained in helping others.

In both these activities the emphasis was on group work, doing the project together around a long table. The charge aide commented that "it takes a while to get them started, especially if they have been sitting around much of the time, but they will take part if you are patient and know that time means something different to them from what it does to a young person."

Group participation was carried farther when the men were given a chance to take more responsibility for planning their work and recreation in the late afternoon and evening. All the patients could not participate in planning, but it could be held up as a goal for those who were more regressed.

The staff felt that the group activities, especially the planning sessions, were successful, in view of some important results. For one thing, the men complained less. For another, they indicated that they did not have to be kept busy all the time in order to feel content. Watching the world go by is a privilege which the older person thinks he has earned, and when this was combined with useful projects that helped other people many of the men felt happy.

Thus, the patients themselves provided a caution to the staff that exuberance for too many planned activities can be overwhelming to the older patient rather than beneficial. Much of the success of the remotivation program in the Family of Elders stemmed from the fact that the staff could accept the men's desire for a slower tempo than that found on other remotivation wards. It was not a place of hustle and bustle, but of measured tread, a community of quiet sharing where there was a feeling of kinship, of doing for each other, regardless of age.

THE VISITORS' CLUB

The main danger of a Family Ward atmosphere lies in the fact that patients will make too great an emotional investment in the ward to the exclusion of thoughts about the world outside. The staff may thus have difficulty in motivating patients toward an interest in taking up life again in the normal community. The "tire doll project" and the making of scrapbooks for children in other hospitals were conscious steps toward counteracting a withdrawal into ward life. Another way of fostering contact with the world outside was through an active program of visiting on the ward by relatives and friends. In this respect Mrs. Harlan was singularly successful, for the number of visitors tripled after she became charge aide in the Family of Elders.

Increase in visiting did not come about by chance, rather it was a planned effort to reach the community, to give new hope to relatives when they went back home, and to prepare the way for acceptance of the patient when he was discharged. Mrs. Harlan felt that it was important that the relatives have a clear picture of the patients' needs as well as knowledge of how those in the community can work with the hospital in meeting these needs more adequately.

Her interest and efforts finally culminated in the formation of a visitors' club, named the H-4 Club by the relatives, after the number of the ward. At the time of the Survey the H-4 Club had been in existence for a year and during that period had become an important instrument of change, not only in improving certain physical aspects of the ward but also in remotivating patients.

First, a word about some of the physical changes. A group of workers, composed of relatives, ward staff, and patients redecorated the dining room, making a comfortable and attractive place for entertaining visitors. The patients themselves built an imitation fireplace so that the room would have a more homelike appearance. Then they made themselves responsible for the flower arrangements, keeping the water fresh and adding new flowers when they were needed. Also, with staff and relative help, they put up bamboo window curtains.

Visitors came to play an important role in preparing for the patients' arts and crafts show which was held each year at Easter and Thanksgiving. The relatives provided special funds for purchasing supplies and an occupational therapy instructor was assigned to the ward once a week. With this help and encouragement some of the patients became quite adept at quick-drying pottery work, painting, and woodcarving. In reality, it was through a group of inveterate patient "whittlers" that craftwork became a regular part of ward activity, for they found in the woodcarving and other handicrafts a release for their energy, as well as a means of recalling forgotten skills. Fortunately, a side room was available which could be made into a handicraft center, and at the time of the Survey the relatives had taken over pottery and art work with the patients.

Members of the H-4 Club contributed in other ways to ward activities. Some relatives took it on themselves to act as trustees of money contributions for cake and ice cream at the parties held on birthdays or holidays. Before the special holidays some of the visitors came to help the men make appropriate decorations, for instance, the Fourth of July flag party and the May Pole party. Once a month there was a Magic Lantern Day, when visitors brought in postcards to be shown to the patients, providing both a contact with the world outside and a nostalgic return to boyhood when the magic lantern took the place of motion pictures or television. One visitor, who played the accordion, donated his time to make old fashioned "squeeze box" music at Magic Lantern Day. Finally, the club set up a car pool in order that elderly visitors who had transportation difficulties could still be able to come to the hospital.

An active visiting program can hurt some patients, if they do not have any relatives or friends who come to see them. However, Mrs. Harlan and the H-4 Club members were aware of this problem and took steps to see that each patient on the ward had a visitor each week even if he did not have relatives. For example, if one patient had three visitors every week, one of them was asked also to spend some of the time with another patient. Mrs. Harlan's intimate knowledge of patient friendship patterns was most valuable in bringing together visitors and patients who would have common interests and would like each other.

COMMENTS AND CONCLUSIONS
An appropriate place to begin our comments about the Family of Elders would be in relation to the discharge pattern, for this is one crucial test of the effectiveness of remotivation efforts. Two-thirds of the patients who were on the ward three years prior to the visit by the observer were still there. The discharges that did take place were mostly in the sixty to seventy age group, but these had been increasing during the last year. For the majority of the patients ward life was the end of the road. Another crucial test of the effectiveness of remotivation is the adjustment of the patients to ward life, for one would hope that if an individual cannot carry on life in the community at least he can have a relatively happy and satisfying life within the hospital. One cannot support the success of adjustment to hospital life with statistics like discharge rates but must depend on more subjective evaluations from staff and relatives. In this respect the Family of Elders was deserving of praise, for those inside and outside the hospital felt that the men were much improved and happier under the remotivation program than in the traditional senile ward organization. Certainly one fact in support of the worth of activities in the Family of Elders is that senile problem patients were being transferred there from other wards for help. There were fewer dramatic changes on this ward than those which occurred in the other situations we are describing in this book, but the subtle beneficial changes were very noticeable.

The important factors in the remotivation might be summed up in the contrast between the terms "senile ward" and the "Family of Elders." A senile ward has connotations of apathy, deterioration, and incontinence. Although one cannot say that such characteristics of behavior were not present in the Family of Elders, the staff made every effort to minimize and eradicate them.

Staff efforts were well reflected in the title of this chapter, for the Family of Elders utilized the best features of the Family Ward, which we described in Chapter 2, without fostering the dependence on the ward situation that could easily preclude an interest in wanting to leave the hospital environment. The family atmosphere was evidenced in many ways; by the fact that the men referred to Mrs. Harlan as "Mom"; through joint efforts in food preparation and "homestyle" service in the dining room; through the making of useful and decorative objects for each other and the ward as a whole; in the flower keeper and the enjoyment of his efforts by all the men; also in the mutual assistance pacts, or the "sick help the sicker" pattern; and finally, through the sharing of visitors in the H-4 Club.

One must also not forget that in the family setting each individual has worth and a place in the scheme of things. Both Mrs. Harlan and her afternoon counterpart had the ability to interest themselves in the problems of individual patients, and to use patient groups for work or recreation in such a way that each individual felt he was contributing to the whole. Most important of all, they and their staff never lost sight of the fact that the main goal was eventual discharge and sought continually to bring evidence of the world outside into the ward environment.

6. Ward Mothers

THE PRECEDING THREE CHAPTERS have dealt with examples of remotivation on wards where the problem of care of mental patients is quite dramatic; that is, where patients have minimal contact with reality, show childlike behavior in terms of body functions, and are unpredictable in relations with other patients and staff. There is another kind of patient who is found in sizable numbers in large mental hospitals. This patient does not show the grossly abnormal behavior of the regressed patient but has not improved sufficiently in getting along with people to make an adjustment to life outside the hospital. He constitutes the bulk of the patient working force, without which most state institutions could not continue to operate. Various hospital industries, like the farm, dairy, shoe shop, or mending room, depend on the skills and efforts which the patient workers, or industrial patients, as they are called, have to offer. In addition, the major housekeeping activities are carried in part by patient workers.

Work can be a valuable therapeutic tool if it is used to strengthen the resources which the patient needs for establishing normal social relations in the community. Too often, however, this treatment goal has been lost by hospital personnel, with the result that patients who are well enough to work but not for discharge, fall into a routine that is far more custodial than therapeutic.

Fortunately, there are encouraging attempts at remotivation among industrial patients, one of which is the subject of this chapter. Our description will differ from that presented previously not only in the type of patient discussed but also in the "before and after" situation which we have been able to reconstruct. The observer talked at some length with the charge aide who had been responsible for an industrial ward, which we have called C-1, prior to a remotivation program. At the time of the Survey visit the remotivation procedures had been in operation for two years but the former charge aide was still on the hospital staff and, in fact, was in charge of another industrial ward. There is every indication that the ward she was administering at the time of the observer's visit was similar to Ward C-1 before remotivation. Her present ward regime and attitudes toward patient care seem to us, therefore, to constitute a valid "before" situation against which we can contrast the "after" situation, the remotivation program on C-1.

The hospital in which these situations were found is located in the western part of the United States, in a warm climate where the emphasis is on agriculture. Although it is a large hospital, many of the buildings are only one story high and are called cottages. In keeping with western architecture, there is a patio outside each ward, with a wall surrounding the patio, a wall high enough so that one can sit on the patio without being seen from the outside, yet low enough so that one can look out when he stands up. The one-story type of construction with patio was most useful in certain of the patients' activities on C-1 when the "new program" was instituted.

LIFE UNDER THE OLD REGIME

Ward C-1 was labeled a continued treatment, open, industrial, adjusted ward. The designation indicated that the door to the ward was not locked; that the patients had reached a level of adjustment that was predictable; that most of the patients were engaged in various jobs throughout the hospital; and that it was a treatment situation rather than merely a custodial one. In fact, the stated aim for C-1 was long-term adjustment of the patient through the work routine.

This happened to be a women's ward. Of the 110 patients, 75 per cent were over forty-five years old and 27 per cent were over seventy. Actually, the age range was from twenty to ninety-one, with the mean age somewhere around sixty. The striking feature was the length of hospital residence, which ranged between three and forty years, with the average at twenty years.

The majority of the women spent six to eight hours each day in jobs off the ward. The laundry, mending room, serving room, and fruit and vegetable garden took care of more than half the workers, while the remainder were classified as helpers in the kitchen, dairy, beauty shop, bakery, canteen, or office. Some were also used as charwomen in the admissions building.

The rest of the patients remained on the ward. Insofar as their age and social adjustment permitted, they were utilized for ward housekeeping activities. Some were classified as regular, meaning dependable, ward workers, who made the beds, washed and waxed the floors, washed the windows, and worked as helpers in the ward dining room. There were a few who had the designation "specific task workers"; that is, one was an "ashtray stand picker-upper," another a "double room caretaker," and still another a "toilet and washroom caretaker." The remark frequently heard about the jobs of the specific task workers was to this effect: "That's all these patients could be expected to do." The end of the worker continuum consisted of the limited or occasional workers, mainly the block pushers and polishers, who walked back and forth, pushing blocks of wood wrapped in cloth, to keep the waxed floor at a high gloss. Each day after breakfast and lunch they went at their task till the floors gleamed.

Not all the women could work, even at simple ward housekeeping tasks. Some were too old or infirm. The remaining group constituted the regular or occasional Bench Warmers, to which we referred in Chapter 2 when we discussed social classification of patients. They merely took up space as far as ward activities were concerned, yet required attention from the staff and other patients at meal- and bedtime.

Routine and Recreation

If one word could be used to characterize the work and ward situation under the old regime on ward C-1 it would be "routine." The women who held jobs in various hospital industries went to the same job day in and day out, as many of them had been doing for years. In addition, the younger ones were expected to double up on work by having responsibility for certain ward tasks at the end of the day. There was always dormitory work to be done, and an endless round of cleaning. Once a week the radiators and mop boards were cleaned and the basement floor scrubbed. Once a month all windows and woodwork were washed. Once a day all rooms and hallways were made neat in appearance, and all soiled linen and clothes were sorted and put in proper place. Also once a day the stairs, washrooms, toilets, and porch were mopped. In all these activities, and many others that were necessary to good housekeeping, the main burden of work fell on the patients, with staff supervision to make certain that the jobs were done correctly. The regular or occasional ward workers were not able to perform all these tasks; hence some of the off-ward industrial workers were utilized.

All ward activities were run according to a detailed schedule, posted in the ward office, and constantly referred to by the charge aide. The ritual of living up to the schedule invited submission of the patients to continuous supervision; for example, checking on clothing, eating, bathing, and leaving the ward.

Recreational programs were not encouraged under this particular ward supervision. By the time most of the women had spent six to eight hours at a hospital job and taken care of their duties on the ward, they had little time or energy left for ward parties or other recreational activities. The ward staff felt that excitement after the work routine was not beneficial, that work itself was the best medicine. It was felt that patients were most comfortable with a strict routine, that order and being busy at a job were better than possible overstimulation by entertainment.

The main impression that the observer carried away after an extended period on the ward was that of order, control, and quiet. The ward had little meaning to the industrial patients other than a place where they ate and slept. The emphasis was on a lack of change, of not wishing to disturb the equilibrium, of maintaining the *status quo*.

Many features of Ward C-1 under the old regime were reminiscent of the Museum Ward described in Chapter 2. The patients on the ward were quite different in terms of adjustment from those in the traditional Museum Ward, but the approach of the staff to patient care was similar. The emphasis on order and quiet, on strict routine, on training for conformity, is the pattern of a Museum Ward. Under this unimaginative regime the ward staff felt secure.

THE REACTIVATION PROGRAM

Remotivation on C-1 was possible in large part because of the effort which the administration and ward personnel had expended on a remotivation project in certain regressed wards a few years earlier. A grant from the state legislature had enabled the hospital to institute a pilot project on selected chronic wards to test the idea that remotivational procedures of the kind we have described in this book are truly beneficial. The results of the pilot project indicated that about twice as many patients were discharged from the pilot study wards as compared with a series of control wards; and, furthermore, that of those still in the hospital, about twice as many from the pilot study wards as from the control wards improved their hospital adjustment. Inasmuch as the pilot study had concentrated on male patients, the next step was to extend hospital effort to chronic female wards. After the experience with women there was sufficient change in the attitudes of hospital personnel toward remotivational procedures and enough aides had been trained in the new techniques to permit further experimentation.

The clinical director decided that the industrial wards needed reorganization in their overall outlook and practice, and selected two wards to spearhead the change in emphasis from "all work and no play" to "some work and some play." The ward situation that constitutes the "after" portion of the description in this chapter was one of the two wards selected by the clinical director.

In order to make the project on the industrial wards successful the clinical director felt it was necessary to increase the staff-patient ratio and replace those ward personnel whose attitude toward industrial patients was rigid, with aides more in tune with remotivational attitudes and procedures.

The next step in carrying out the new plans for C-1 was to gather a group of patients, holding certain women from the previous ward group and transferring more from other wards in the hospital. Of these new patients who were transferred from other wards, about one-third came from the acute, intensive treatment building. They had not responded well to the somatic therapies after a three- to four-month period, but were no longer grossly disturbed and were judged ready for hospital industry. The rest of the transfer patients came from a variety of closed and semi-open wards for either disturbed or convalescing patients. They had been patients in the hospital for a longer time and their overtly psychotic behavior had subsided, although their skill in social relationships had not improved sufficiently for return to the community.

These patients appeared at first glance to be well. However, nearly one-half of them had had no contact with the outside world since their admission to the hospital. The rest ranged in degree of contact with normal society from occasional letter writing to regular visits from relatives and friends. Those whose contact was minimal or nonexistent had come to accept the indifference of relatives and friends and turned themselves increasingly toward acceptance of hospital life. This was especially true of those who were holdovers from the old regime on C-1. When the holdovers first came to C-1, at some time prior to 1952, many of them had been ready for boarding home care. However, they had not been placed outside the hospital and their dependence on ward life had been fostered by the attitude of the staff that the patients were better off where they were and were not well enough to leave anyway.

Many of the women who formed the new patient group on C-1, that is, the group organized for the reactivation (their word for remotivation) program, conceded that they were well enough to take care of themselves but felt that they had lost the necessary social skills for making an adjustment in the world outside the hospital. Thus, there was a formidable barrier of attitudes in the women themselves that faced those who were responsible for remotivation procedures.

Another characteristic of the new patient group should be kept in mind. The age range was now twenty-two to sixty-three years, with the goal of having no patient over sixty. The mean age was thirty-five, in contrast to an average of about sixty before the reactivation plans were put into operation. The length of residence also had changed, now ranging from four months to fifteen years, with an average length of stay of five years. This was in keeping with the administrative policy which we mentioned above, of making the ward into a more realistic treatment unit.

Step 1: Job Evaluation and Ward Improvement

The patient work pattern was the place where new procedures were first introduced, with a review by the ward staff and physician of jobs both on the ward and in hospital industry. Emphasis was on variety of job experience and progressive job experience, and the time spent each week at a job was determined on the basis of the patient's age, social adjustment, and needs. As a result, some patients were shifted to longer working hours, that is, more than twenty hours a week, whereas some were scheduled for less than twenty hours a week.

At the time of the Survey visit the procedure of job assignment worked rather informally, dictated in part by the decision about the needs of each patient, by the requirements of different departments of the hospital, and in part by the relationship which the charge aide had with various hospital service and maintenance departments. The charge aide's biggest problem had been to convince the various departments that they should make a job analysis of their requirements, planning on the use of at least two patients for each job that would ordinarily be filled by one worker who was not a patient. Because of the charge aide's interest in job analysis, her knowledge of her patients, and her good relationships with other hospital personnel, the patients had all been placed relatively well.

The principles of variety of job experience and progressive job experience could be expressed by saying that an attempt was made to provide a variety of work experiences for each patient that also proceeded toward the acceptance of greater and greater responsibility by the patient. Variety was afforded by having some patients work part time in the mending room and part time in the kitchen; others would work part time in the beauty shop and part time in the garden. Different jobs for a given patient were related in that they had similar skill requirements and were selected because they were congenial to her. Work variety tended to relieve the monotony as well as to prevent a patient from becoming obsessively attached to one type of job, as in the old days on the ward.

As patients improved in their social and work adjustment they were shifted to other jobs in which they had both skill and interest, but which required that they take correspondingly more responsibility. This was a direct attack on the trend of the hospital to become too desirable a place for a psychotic patient, because of the emphasis on dependency. For many patients the growth of responsibility was painful, yet a necessary step in their recovery.

Job responsibility was also transferred to the ward situation, where all patients had certain housekeeping work and where ward improvement projects brought a sense of working together for common goals. For the housekeeping duties, groups of five, six, or eight patients worked as dormitory helpers, hall and linen closet helpers, clothesroom helpers, and helpers for the small dormitories and side rooms. Saturday was designated cleaning day, at which time 40 patients would help to get the job done. The charge aide commented that the patients preferred to do some housework, especially since they were allowed to keep some of their personal belongings near them. Assignments of ward work by the staff were rarely made, and then only for the few Bench Warmers.

Ward improvement projects not only aimed at increasing the feeling of responsibility on the part of individual patients but also represented a concerted effort to change the ward environment. The first step had been a rearrangement of the ward furniture, changing it from the rigid grouping, like that found on the Museum Ward, to informal groupings, especially around big tables. At first, the women were uncomfortable with the new arrangement and repeatedly moved the furniture back to its traditional place, but with encouragement and staff approval, they came to accept it and like it.

Use of patient help to make things for the ward followed. There were new curtains, bedspreads, seat covers to be made, all of which was done around the big tables. Inasmuch as many of the patients were working off the ward less than twenty hours a week, they had more time for ward improvement projects.

The results of the first step in reactivation, reevaluation of jobs and an attempt to change the environment on the ward, were twofold. First, there was a growing feeling of identification with the ward as a social group, an increased feeling of pride in C-1 as a place to live. Second, there was a reawakening of the pleasures of social interaction. While sitting around the tables making things to improve the appearance of their ward, the women began to talk to each other as they had never done before. It was as if a group of apartment dwellers, who formerly had only nodded to each other in passing, were suddenly thrown together in close association, and for the first time began to find out what their neighbors were like.

Step 2: Activities and Planning

The reawakened need and pleasure in social interaction provided the basis for the next step in reactivation, which began with an emphasis on social activities of a recreational nature and led to a greater participation by the patients in planning and carrying out their various activities. The staff did not initiate these changes quickly, but were willing to wait until the new pleasure in social relations had been maintained for a number of months. Once they felt that this gain had been consolidated and the patients were socially secure in each other's presence, they urged the women to acquire more experience in meeting people who did not live on the ward. At first, this urging was directed toward women from other wards, later toward men. Because the patients were in contact with women from other wards in the course of their hospital jobs, it was not too difficult to get a varied group of patient visitors together for a party on C-1.

Again, when this gain in social relationships had been consolidated, the women were encouraged to ask men from other wards to attend their parties. Here it was that the patio outside the ward proved to be very useful. A "Patio Dance" was held, to which men and women from other wards were invited, an event which was so successful that it became an institution and a favorite activity of the patients during the summer months.

The growing enjoyment of social activities and increased willingness to take responsibility for both work and recreation made it possible for the staff to shift much of the planning of activities to patient groups. In terms of time sequence, this level of patient improvement was reached about a year and a half after the reactivation program was first put into operation. Two patient organizations which developed gradually were especially instrumental in planning activities. The first was called simply Patients' Meeting. It began as a monthly gathering of all the patients on the ward for singing or looking at slides or a similar activity, but more and more it took on the aspects of a patient government organization. An extension of the Patients' Meeting soon appeared, called a Planning Committee, which met once a week and was composed of a group of approximately 20 patients. They met with certain of the ward staff to make plans for weekly ward activities and had as their specific aim to reduce patient stagnation in social interaction and to counteract the familiar "do it for me" attitude. The Planning Committee became one of the most important of the patient groups and the main agency for planning and carrying out ward activities.

At this point we should interrupt our chronological account of the reactivation process on Ward C-1 to provide some illustrations of patient activities. A sample of ward activities for October of 1954 is a good beginning, the month that C-1 was studied as part of the Survey. This is shown in Chart 3.

Note should be taken of the fact that each month the charge aide on ward C-1 prepared a monthly report similar to that in Chart 3. It was then discussed and evaluated with the rest of the ward staff and the physician in charge of treatment.

The outstanding feature of the activities during October was the organizing of classes in ballet and classical music. In each case a patient started the project, recruited her class, and planned the procedure for each session.

CHART 3. SAMPLE OF ACTIVITIES ON WARD C-1 IN OCTOBER, 1954

Activity	Remarks	Number of sessions	Participation Active	Audience	New
Planning Committee	Patient planning for weekly ward activity	4	21		4
Goal Clubs	Established for patients who are not improving. Motivational reading, simple exercises and games, music, rhythm band	2	18	9	7
Sunshine Club	Entirely run and governed by patients. Occasionally serve refreshments. Present project, needlework	3	18		4
Poetry Reading	A weekly group who read poetry aloud to each other. Varied selections are chosen. Group prefers humorous readings. Out of this group has evolved the Verse Speaking Choir	4	9		3
Verse Speaking Choir	Special Project: "Little Orphan Annie," planned as a special feature for the Halloween Party	5	11		1
Literature Reading	A weekly group who read and discuss books and special articles	4	11		2
Patients' Meeting	All patients called together. Kodachrome slides of recent Hawaiian Party. Very successful evening	1	60		6
Ward Activity	Making Halloween Party decorations	13	11		5
Party Rehearsal	Dancers, witches, and other characters for Halloween Party	1	14		
Informal Recreation	Table games, cards, jig saw puzzles, etc.	3	7		1
Gardening	Planning, preparing soil, and planting fall garden	3	7		3
Folk Dance (With patient orchestra)	Held on C-1 with patients from other wards invited as guests, male patients included. Under sponsorship of recreational therapist	4	32	35	5
Classes under Leadership	A class instigated and taught: (1) Ballet by a former dance teacher	3	8	2	1
	(2) Record concert, classical music interpreted	2	7		

More detailed examples of recreational activities are to be found in the description of a barbecue held during August and an Hawaiian party in July of 1954. The barbecue took place in the evening on the patio adjoining C cottage. There were "hot dogs" with mustard and relish, punch, and potato salad, all prepared by patients on the food committee, and toasted marshmallows to finish the meal. Portable charcoal stoves had been set up on the patio, over which all the cooking and toasting was done. Background music from the phonograph provided a pleasant atmosphere throughout the evening. After supper the recreational therapist supervised games, such as table tennis, badminton, ring toss, horse shoes, volley ball, and croquet.

Altogether 60 patients enjoyed the barbecue, 35 of them played the games, while 12 could be counted as a participating audience. Many comments were heard from the women to the effect that they loved the whole affair and wanted to have another barbecue soon.

The Hawaiian party entailed greater responsibility, initiative, and imagination on the part of the patients than that required for the barbecue. As patients from Ward C-1 gathered, and guests from other wards and the administrative staff began to arrive, they heard soft Hawaiian music. One of the patients was responsible for the operation of the record player and all background music during the program. Another patient sang greetings to the arriving guests and placed leis around their necks. When all were assembled one of the women opened the program by reading a poetic description of Hawaii, which was followed by a musical selection, "Hawaiian Rhythms," played by the C-1 rhythm band in time with a phonograph record. The nine patients in the rhythm band then became a Verse Speaking Choir to read "Dream Island" by Don Blanding. This was followed by a pantomime play, written by one of the patients and entitled "All Aboard for Hawaii." It was in two acts, with one of the patients as the narrator. Between the acts the rhythm band provided more music. After the play six costumed dancers presented a hula dance, then there were refreshments, appropriately called luau. An invitation to the luau was extended by an authentically costumed hostess, a patient, who asked the guests to come to the dining room, magnificently decorated with flowers and fruit. Refreshments were served by the hula dancers, who also put on a spontaneous floor show for the guests while they were eating. At nine o'clock, an hour and a half after beginning, the party ended and the patient clean-up committee took over.

All the work for the Hawaiian party was done by the patients, assisted and directed by the aides on the ward. The patients made the hand-painted costumes, the rhythm band instruments, leis, programs, and scenery. They arranged the flowers which were provided by the hospital nursery. Altogether 24 patients played an active part in the program itself.

A year and a half after the reactivation program was begun on C-1, much of the detail of arranging for patient activity and recreation was handled by the patients themselves. The barbecue and Hawaiian party were examples of the increased responsibility which they had come to accept. One result of this shift toward greater social responsibility was the increase in numbers of hospital staff and visitors from the community who came to the ward at the invitation of patients. In turn, there was an increase in the number of patients who went to town on pass. Another result of the increased social responsibility was the formation of a Patient Reception Committee. It was the function of this committee to explain to each new patient what would be expected of her on the ward and to introduce her to the rest of the women.

There was a third result of the growth in responsibility, a shift in the control functions on the ward from the staff more toward the patients. The social pressures which patients applied to each other became by far the most important sources of control rather than the reprimands and bestowed rewards of the ward staff.

The final result of patient growth in social relationships could be found in the staff. They felt that the traditional organization of the ward, charge aide, aide, and attendant, was not in keeping with the changing social reality of the patient group. The traditional organization was directed down toward the patient; yet the patients were demonstrating an ability to take responsibility on more of an equal than a subordinate basis. At this point the remotivation program moved into the next phase.

Step 3: Ward Mothers

The 11 aides who comprised the total for C-1 on both the morning and afternoon shifts were designated Section Leaders, each one being made responsible for 10 patients. The suggestion for utilizing the aides in this manner originally came from the ward charge aide, who had noted that many of the patients called her "Mom" and frequently came to her for advice. The physician in charge of the ward accepted the idea on an experimental basis and the 11 patient-groups were formed. Each aide was to be responsible for the daily life of her patients, to see to their bathing and dressing, to help them select their clothes, to assist them in making decisions about social events, and to help them in plans for ward activities.

When the observer visited C-1 the Section Leader system had been in operation for only a short time, and all its therapeutic implications were not yet apparent to those on the staff who were closest to the situation. However, by talking with various staff members as well as many patients, and carefully observing ward activity, he was able to gain a picture of the chain of events following the introduction of Section Leaders and also to make certain interpretations as to the meaning of the Section Leaders or "Ward Mothers," as he quickly came to call them.

Certain results of the change in ward administration followed almost immediately. The need for attachment to a well person, dormant in every patient and held down by the lack, or ineffective distribution, of ward personnel, now could be openly expressed. Within two weeks to a month each group had solidified around its leader. This was not unaccompanied by anxiety, for not only was there the fear of any permanent attachment, a common feeling in the psychotic, but there was also remembrance of turnover in the past among ward personnel. Many patients were afraid that they might lose their stable Leader, these desertion fears making them hypersensitive to certain events on the ward. There was a tendency to watch rather jealously the behavior of their Section Leader and to become anxious and upset when she left the ward or moved toward another section group. The jealous feelings were also directed toward the other members of the section, then later toward members of other sections. Some fights even developed between patients. The stabilization of feeling regarding each other and other groups took about three more weeks.

With the diminishment of separation anxiety and jealousy, individual patients moved to a new level of social maturity. They began to look after themselves; some increased their ability to share activities with others; some discussed their work more with other patients and their Section Leader. Gradually they began to function more like a large family and to assume shared and reciprocal responsibilities.

In the major problems of adjustment to new hospital jobs, or responsibility for ward recreational programs, or in the many minor irritations and frustrations of each day, the role of the Section Leader, or Ward Mother, seemed most helpful. Not only was more attention given to the patients' clothing and grooming but the patients were reminded informally that they had to divide up their day and remember their appointments, that they would no longer be escorted to and from work, or to recreation events in other parts of the hospital. Patients learned more about the effect of praise and blame, for both emotions now came from an individual to whom they had a close personal attachment. There was the effect of their intimate group as well, which acted on the one hand to support them through anxious moments, while on the other it applied strict sanctions against deviant behavior. Finally, both the patient group and the Section Leader became the testing ground where the individual could try out new approaches in interpersonal relations before trying them on less familiar people.

It seemed to the observer that one factor contributing to the success of the Ward Mothers was their ability to minister to a sequence of arising needs on the part of the patients rather than tell each patient what she needed. For example, in the matter of work the emphasis was shifted from the idea that the patient needed work to interest in the meaningfulness of work for the patient. Activities were not measured by whether they were productive or unproductive, but whether they had meaning.

An interview with the young physician who was in charge of C-1 brought out another feature of the Section Leader program by pointing to a problem that had been created by the reactivation program. Although the majority of patients had benefited from the job evaluation and increased responsibility for ward events, some had not been able to take the pressure for improved social adjustment. Their adjustment became worse and it was necessary to transfer them to a more conservative ward. Although the number of discharges to the community had nearly doubled, the number of transfers to the closed wards had also increased. Such a turn of events was a matter of some concern to the staff and the psychiatrist looked to the Section Leader plan with the hope that it might help the more anxious patients increase their social stability without frightening them appreciably. He suggested that the feeling of belongingness engendered toward the Section Leader was one of the most important aspects of the situation. The patient no longer need feel that she was just another patient, but rather that she had an adviser on whom she could rely. For example, when the question of grounds privileges or a pass to town came up, the patient would first discuss it with her Section Leader and then with the doctor.

To continue with the reactivation program in general, the psychiatrist indicated that the combination of patient-aide group units, patient-planned recreational activities, and staff-planned industrial activities covered many major areas of ego-strengthening experience. It had the advantage of coming close to what life on the outside of the hospital is like, yet offering a certain amount of protection. Furthermore, it allowed the development of interpersonal stresses, but provided a means by which the individual could get help in handling them.

An important side effect of the Section Leader plan concerned the reaction of the aides themselves. The psychiatrist laid special emphasis on this, not only because he and others on the medical staff were pleased with the superior job the aides had done, but also because of the effect on their job attitudes. First, there was a noticeable increase in their morale and interest in their job. No longer would they say, "I have nothing to report," at the weekly ward meetings on treatment review. Furthermore, the aides decided to keep daily reports on their patient groups and to note the nature of each patient's participation in ward activities. When the question of discharge for one of their patients arose, they had much valuable information in their daily reports to contribute to the decision.

The aides had come to feel that they were part of a concerted effort to help patients, and also realized that they were learning a lot in addition. In looking back over the formation of the sections, the psychiatrist commented that they had been fortunate in having insisted on both patient and aide preference as to whom they would like to be with. It so happened that each section had at least one member that was not picked by an aide or one member who had not chosen that aide. Nobody could thus complain of having received all the Crocks (the poor treatment prospects in ward language) on the ward.

COMMENTS AND CONCLUSIONS

Not only was this chapter different from those preceding it in the type of patient discussed, it introduced a new factor in the treatment process. Personality was still an important item in this process, although now it was in the form of the 11 Section Leaders or Ward Mothers, as we prefer to call them, rather than depending on the personality of one person, like Mrs. Cosgrove or Mrs. Harlan. The diffusion of effort permitted the development of a much greater sense of belongingness than in a situation where there were 100 patients in a group instead of 10. Knowing that one belongs to someone else is an important feeling at any stage in life, but in terms of the hospital experience we think it is especially important for those who really think they are well enough for the outside world yet lack courage and resourcefulness. The security achieved through the close relationship with the Ward Mother often might be the difference between continued hospitalization and discharge.

Equal emphasis must also be placed on the effect of the Section or Family on the individual patient. It is doubtful if this effect would be as important with patients who were more regressed in

their social relationships, yet for the industrial patient membership in the group had much to teach about the sharing of affection, the meaning of emotional support from friends, and the
reality of group pressures to conform to socially acceptable
behavior. Furthermore, the groups or "families" on C-1 were in
daily contact, and for much longer periods each day than in
regular group therapy sessions. Indeed, they were more like
families than any other kind of group.

The reactivation program on C-1 showed some of the problems
that must be faced in devising remotivation programs for industrial patients. One of these concerns patient jobs. It was difficult
at first to get hospital departments to accept patient workers on
less than a full-time basis and to analyze their job requirements
in terms of two patients to every well person needed. Administrative personnel in the various departments were still inclined to
view jobs as jobs and not as means toward patient discharge or
improvement. It was equally difficult to get the ward staff to
release good ward workers for employment in hospital industry.
The habit patterns that stress a neat and shining ward as one of
the most important variables in patient care do not change easily
to an emphasis on the needs of each individual patient. These
problems are unique to industrial wards and indicate the magnitude of the problem in changing attitudes of hospital personnel so
that work can become meaningful to the individual rather than
just a way of getting certain tasks done.

Finally, we would point out again, as we did at the conclusion
of the House of Miracles, that in the remotivation of mental
patients, one improvement leads to another. This has two aspects.
On the one hand, it cautions against trying to move too fast with
patients. If they are not ready for the next step, one's efforts can
be wasted. On the other hand, it signals encouragement, for
when one solid gain has been established the whole situation is
changed and both patients and staff think of new things to try.

7. "Cafeteria Training"

IT GOES WITHOUT SAYING that patients at different levels of social adjustment require different remotivational techniques. When dealing with the incontinent, withdrawn patient it is important to emphasize training in simple bodily functions like elimination, and to work on personal appearance and eating habits. Adequate functioning in these areas is basic to the acceptance of the individual in normal social groups. When the patient shows benefit from the habit training procedures, effort can then be directed toward the use of simple activities that emphasize mutual effort and social communication. As the patient improves in his ability to get along with other patients and staff members he can be given tasks that require the assumption of individual responsibility and the making of decisions. Later, this can take the form of job activities off the ward and planning for recreational and other social activities in cooperation with the other patients on the ward.

The preceding chapters have dealt with ward situations at various levels along the continuum of social adjustment, beginning in Chapter 3 with basic habit training and presenting in Chapter 6 the industrial patient who may soon be ready for discharge. In each of our case presentations hospital effort was directed primarily at one level of social adjustment, or in other words, at one type of patient.

The eventual success of modifying the social milieu for the remotivation of mental patients lies in a program that is geared to patients at all levels of adjustment, and changes in emphasis as the individual patient gets better. In essence, this means the integration of treatment facilities throughout the hospital, and the close cooperation of both medical and nonmedical staff on all kinds of wards. The idea of a "flow chart" in which all wards in the hospital have a specific place, expresses the concept of overall hospital remotivation from an organizational standpoint.

Large state mental hospitals have been concerned for so long with the exigencies of the physical care of patients that it has been next to impossible to organize the staff for a complete remotivational effort. For one thing, the number and quality of personnel required has been a severe obstacle. For another, rigid attitudes toward patients as exemplified in the Legend of Chronicity are not easy to change. It is not surprising, then, that the Survey did not find an example of total hospital effort directed toward remotivation in a large state institution. However, there was one situation that appeared to the observer to have the basic ingredients for a hospitalwide program of planning and action in the social remotivation of patients. At the time of visit in April of 1954 there were few staff members who saw the possibilities for an integrated effort on all levels. However, when the observer finished his visit on different wards in this hospital, he saw the facts fitting into a pattern that was of broader scope than any recognized by the personnel who were caring for patients. This presentation seems to us, therefore, to be an important one because of its implications for long-range planning in patient care in mental hospitals.

Our story is based in a large hospital in the eastern part of the United States, which we have called St. Charles Hospital. The patient population was approximately 6,500, of whom some 900 were men and women who had forgotten or rejected their habits of personal hygiene, social customs, and traditional patterns of everyday activities. Like so many hospitals of its kind, buildings were overcrowded and old; facilities for feeding the patients and providing recreation were far less than one would desire. Yet in the early months of 1952 some remodeling of existing buildings took place, a fact which might be considered the event that initiated the active remotivation program. It is on the basis of these two factors; first, the presence of large numbers of regressed patients and, second, the remodeling program, that our story begins.

FROM STAGNATION TO LIFE

Early in March of 1952 approximately 270 patients were transferred from the A building at St. Charles to certain wards in the B building which had just been remodeled. In particular, 100 of these patients, all women, were assigned to Wards B-1 and B-2. Using hospital parlance, the women were characterized as regressed and vegetable-like, noisy, destructive, and dirty. They were sent to B-1 and B-2 for concentrated efforts at habit training, an aim that was described by the clinical director of the hospital as follows: "It was necessary to set up this intensive rehabilitation program in order to get these people off the floor, teach them to wear clothes, live like people instead of animals, and to restore to them the self-respect they once had." In very simple terms the original purpose of the habit training was the improvement of a stagnant patient population.

There were both weaknesses and strengths present in the situation at the very beginning. The weaknesses were in the area of staff attitudes, an honest expression of the Legend of Chronicity. Even though the patients were to be rehabilitated the aides continued to think of them as poor prognostic cases; once chronic, always chronic. These attitudes meant that there was little motivation for the aides to offer more than the necessary custodial care even in the new (that is, remodeled) setting. Initially, the effect of the attitudes was complicated by suspicions toward any action which the medical or nursing staff might take because of recent disciplinary action against an aide in the building.

The means of overcoming both the attitudes about patients and suspicions about administrative staff lay in a reorganization of the nursing service in the hospital which had taken place a short time previous to the transfer of patients to B-1 and B-2. Certain aspects of the reorganization related to the appointment of a First Assistant Head Nurse, who was responsible for nursing activities throughout the hospital as they related to patient care and treatment. Being relieved from concerns about education or administration, she had time to devote her energies to the ward situation and to plan with the medical staff and the aides for changes in existing treatment programs. It was most fortunate that the First Assistant Head Nurse realized her primary task was to build strong rapport with the ward staff, including the ward physician and the aides. Rather than criticizing the latter group for their handling of the "untidy" patients, she attempted to see the problem from their point of view and act accordingly.

The other strength lay in the fact that many of the occupational therapy activities had fallen to the nursing department. There was no director of occupational therapy for some months, and when one was appointed she found nurses carrying on many of the occupational therapy activities on the wards. Bringing these activities to the ward situation facilitated the remotivation activities on closed wards.

The decision to utilize Wards B-1 and B-2 for an intensive program of habit training was made originally by the clinical director of the hospital, the chief nurse, and the chief of the women's service after they had consulted with the physician in charge of the wards. The First Assistant Head Nurse acted then as the intermediary between the top administrative staff and those on the wards who were directly responsible for patient care.

We have noted that at the outset, that is, in March of 1952, the patients presented rather severe problems in care, for they were incontinent, destructive, and in many instances unable to feed themselves. The formal diagnostic picture covered a wide range, although various types of schizophrenia accounted for about three-quarters of the group. The second largest group was designated psychosis with mental deficiency; the rest presented a variety of conditions. Half the women were under fifty years of age, but only a few were over seventy.

On her first contact with the ward the First Assistant Head Nurse found it as well run as could be expected under the circumstances. The staff were trying to train the patients to take baths twice a week, which helped to raise the level of patient care, but the sheer problem of maintaining a minimum level of cleanliness took most of the ward personnel's time.

In spite of remodeling, the dayroom appeared rather bleak and uncomfortable. The paint was drab in color. Although magazines were provided on occasion, no other touch of the outside world reached the majority of patients. There was no radio or television set. Most of the women sat around the porch or day hall with almost no constructive activity offered them.

This is the background, then, of Wards B-1 and B-2 at the beginning of habit training. With demonstraton of sincere interest on the part of the First Assistant Head Nurse, and willing response from some of the aides, efforts were turned to basic habit training. To this end the ward staff worked for almost a year.

They wanted improvement in three areas: toilet training, cleanliness, and feeding habits. For the first two of these the techniques utilized were the same as those we have described for other ward situations, especially in the third and fourth chapters: The Habit Training Ward and The House of Miracles. Repetition of these procedures would serve no useful purpose here. A word is in order, however, about improvement in feeding habits. The eating arrangement on B-1 and B-2 was a cafeteria, for those patients who could make use of cafeteria facilities. The majority had to be fed from trays prepared in advance by the staff, some even had to be spoon-fed. A great deal of staff time was spent at mealtime alone, getting trays ready for patients and then feeding many of them. If an improvement in patient abilities in feeding habits could be brought about, staff time could be released for other activities on the ward. In other words, if patients could be taught to go through a cafeteria line, then feed themselves, aides would have more time available to work with patients on other remotivational procedures. The third part of the habit training came to be known then as "cafeteria training."

The habit training routine produced results in some of the patients. When a group of the women had become continent, could eat as a group in the ward cafeteria, and were willing to do simple ward tasks, they were transferred to wards where the patients in general showed a higher level of skill in social interaction. In other words, they were transferred to "tidy" wards. With six months of intensive habit training, groups of five or six patients at approximately the same level of tidiness and work capacity were transferred.

By early January of 1953, some nine months after the transfer of patients from the A area to B-1 and B-2, it became apparent that success of the program of habit training was only fleeting. Many of the patients who had been transferred to better wards were returned because they had become "untidy" again. The clinical director of the hospital explained this process when he said that the patient who is transferred to a "tidy" ward easily gets lost in the crowd. In a short time she is found once again on the floor, feet drawn up, head down, incontinent, and desperately trying to escape from the world. Here was a crisis. As later events proved, it was a fortunate crisis, for out of it grew the next important step in remotivation at St. Charles Hospital.

Changes in Remotivation: The Sequence of Events

The change in emphasis of remotivation activities on B-2 was not planned carefully in advance; rather, it developed as patient interest was aroused and the ward staff saw new ways to channel the activities of patients. The initial factor in the change was premeditated, however, this being a careful survey of all the patients on B-1 and B-2, begun during the first week in January, 1953. The First Assistant Head Nurse and the ward physician interviewed each patient on the wards in alphabetical order, evaluating the present status of the patient and making some judgment as to her therapeutic possibilities. They utilized a three-fold classification, as follows: Group 1 (10 patients) consisted of those patients who were functioning at a level sufficiently high to be in recreational therapy off the ward and in group psychotherapy. They were able to express themselves adequately, were in reasonable contact with reality, and did ward work. Patients in Group 2 (25 patients) were functioning well enough to read and participate in informal social interaction. With help it was felt that they might improve sufficiently for activities off the ward. In Group 3 (73 patients) were most of the senile or mentally deficient patients, along with those who were still seriously regressed in behavior. It was felt that they might continue to benefit from habit training and perhaps from more advanced remotivational procedures. There were a number of patients in Group 3 who had shown marked improvement when habit training procedures were first introduced, had been transferred to "tidy" wards, but had relapsed and been returned to B-2. For those in Group 3 a longer trial period of observation was necessary before making a more accurate judgment about therapeutic possibilities.

At the same time that the patient survey was being conducted the staff-patient ratio was changed from one aide or attendant for every 25 patients to one for every 15. This meant that activities for patients over and above the demands of physical care could be increased.

Toward the end of January music therapy was introduced, the first session being an hour of symphony recordings. When the hour was concluded, the patients were asked to suggest their favorite songs, and six such requests were made. Later more requests were made and hillbilly music, marches, and religious music became great favorites. Using the results of research at Eloise State Hospital in Michigan, music was later presented in sequence, beginning with marches, then intermezzo, harmony, and, finally, folk and dance numbers.

From the beginning it was obvious that the patients were responding to the music, especially the hillbilly type. Many began to clap in rhythm, others to dance. Even those who were the most regressed could be seen responding by hand, foot, or body movements. Therefore, the music hours were continued at a specific time each week and became an established part of the general remotivation program.

A few weeks after the introduction of music a group of 10 patients were selected for concentrated nursing care, with special emphasis on personal hygiene, grooming, and greater social interaction. This was the beginning of what we have called "expanded cafeteria training," or what was called "long-table retraining" by the hospital staff. Those selected for the original group of 10 were patients who had been judged to have a favorable therapeutic outlook on the ward patient survey. The emphasis was on group activities, eating together, washing together, and entering into joint activities around a long table (often formed by putting two or three smaller tables together). Originally, the participation of members of the group in activities around the long table was sought by working on projects that would contribute to the comfort of the ward. For example, drapery material was obtained from the occupational therapy department. With the help of the aides, the patients made the draperies and hung them, and from the material left over made a number of cushions.

We will come back to a fuller discussion of the activities around the long table after we have described the sequence of events in the second stage of remotivation at St. Charles Hospital. A word is in order at this point, however, about the activities of the First Assistant Head Nurse, concerning the concentrated care for the group of 10 patients. As mentioned earlier, one of the difficulties to be overcome on both B-1 and B-2 was a rigidity of attitudes by the aides regarding potentiality for patient improvement. The First Assistant Head Nurse was wise enough to know that she could not change these attitudes by quoting theories, but would need to demonstrate in a nonthreatening manner certain practical ways of working with patients. Group efforts at personal hygiene and grooming and group work around a table on a common project were practical ways of dealing with the patients, and improvement of the ward furnishings could be appreciated by staff as well as patients. The decision of the nurse to use practical demonstration in place of theory quickly counteracted staff inertia, and on the sewing project the staff took the initiative for seeing it completed.

Concentrated efforts toward a small group of patients did not mean that the bulk of the women on the wards were neglected. With the help of the occupational and recreational therapy departments, games were introduced for an hour twice a week. At first they were simple games like Button, Button, Who's Got the Button. Then movies were started and were shown every Saturday; they brought a surprising reaction from the patients. Bingo for those who were in sufficient contact with reality to participate, and simplified handball games on the porch offered further stimulation.

The original group of 10 patients selected for intensive training came from B-2, but in a few months a similar group was chosen on B-1 and the group on B-2 was expanded. By the fall of 1953 the intensive activation of patients with group procedures was extended to all the patients on the two wards who showed the ability to participate. At the very least, all the patients were *exposed* to more activities. The number and complexity of the games was increased, a piano was purchased, and group singing was encouraged.

When the results of the general and concentrated reactivation programs were considered in November of 1953, eight patients had been placed on trial visit at home and five others had been transferred to another ward where there was more emphasis on occupational therapy activities off the ward. Of the other patients on the wards all but 16 had shown definite improvement in washing, grooming, and toileting problems. About 15 had shown marked improvement, 50 some improvement, and the rest showed improvement in one segment of activity, at least in an increased alertness to their surroundings.

By the time of the Survey visit in April of 1954, two other factors had entered the picture as far as Wards B-1 and B-2 were concerned. For one thing, six psychiatric aides had been assigned to the area, each aide being responsible for 15 to 17 patients. It was the job of the aide to see that her patients were properly dressed, bathed regularly, and received the benefit of regular grooming and personal hygiene procedures. Each aide's group ate together, sitting each time at the same tables so that they could establish a routine.

The assignment of one aide to a specific group of patients had some features in common with the Ward Mother program that we described in the previous chapter. However, the St. Charles program never developed so fully as the Ward Mother undertaking on the industrial ward, one reason being that the level of patient ability in the social sphere was much lower on Wards B-1 and B-2 than at the western hospital. The emphasis was more on the establishment of routines in the areas of personal hygiene and feeding than on the development of close interpersonal relationships. The two situations were similar, however, in making it possible for a member of the ward staff to become increasingly familiar with the needs of specific patients, also in giving the patient the security of a familiar face every day.

The second factor was a growing awareness on the part of the hospital administration that they could shift the basic habit training procedures more and more to the A area of the hospital. This was the great reservoir of regressed and untidy patients and, therefore, the logical place for initial steps in toilet training, cleanliness, and feeding. When the patients had reacted favorably to the habit training, they could be transferred to B-1 and B-2, or other wards of a similar nature in the B area. Here they could be given the group reactivation as practiced around the long tables, which hopefully would then lead to added improvement. However, before carrying the implications of this decision any farther we should describe in more detail the group work around the long tables.

"The Ladies of the Long Table"

The distinguishing feature of "long-table retraining" was that the activity to be performed, be it making a quilt, or a doll, or simple utensils for the ward, was broken down into its component parts. Each part, or step in the process, would then be given to one or two or three patients. The end result of the step-by-step process was a finished product. The advantages in this approach to group activity were that more individual occupations could be created; patients could get a task that fitted their present level of behavior or interest, and they could see that out of a series of activities a good result could come.

The more the observer thought about long-table retraining, the more he thought it had something in common with the earlier efforts at habit training, for it was similar to training patients to move along a cafeteria food counter in line and assemble a complete meal. It seemed only natural that the term which had been used by the ward staff for the habit training procedure, "cafeteria training," should also be applied to the work around the long tables.

An example of a task which was broken down into "cafeteria training" was the making of soft balls from burlap bags. Step 1 consisted of pulling the burlap bag apart by threads, then the threads were tied together in a long string. In Step 3 the string was rolled up to form a ball. In Step 4 it was covered with some kind of material to keep the string in place, and, finally, the edges of this material were sewn together to keep it firm. The product was a ball which could be used for ward games without the danger of hurting anyone, if it accidentally (or purposely) hit her.

Certain aspects of pulling burlap were most beneficial to a particular type of patient known as the Fringer, who constantly unraveled her own clothes. Unraveling burlap bags provided an outlet for the energy that had formerly been directed toward her own apparel and, in addition, directed it to a useful end that the patient could appreciate.

A different example could be found in painting paper plates. In cafeteria training this became: (1) overall painting of plates, (2) cutting out pictures for decoration, (3) pasting of pictures on plate, (4) outlining picture with white art paint, (5) shellacking plate for durability. The end result was decorative and added color to the dayroom without danger of breakage and injury.

Further illustration of "cafeteria training," as seen through the eyes of an aide on the ward, came from an interview with the observer. The following statement does not constitute her exact words but is a reconstruction of the main points she made.

We use it [cafeteria training] for rolling up and weaving strips for rugs, cutting patterns, and so forth. We permit regressed patients to use scissors, dull tips you know, but we've had no bad accidents, even when a patient gets disturbed. We were scared all right when we started this, but now I don't know why we were. I think of the time when I saw a patient make a sharp knife out of a spoon and cut himself; that was when we used spoons and no knives and forks, for safety sake. Well, it's less dangerous to use scissors. When you don't hold patients down too much they pay you more mind and behave better, I believe.

Well, the regressed patients cut up strips of cloth at the table, and a couple of other patients at the table cut them into tiny pieces and put them in a box. They are the angry patients, they like to cut it seems. Then a bunch of other patients at a table nearby make cloth dolls or animals, using the cut-up material for stuffing. Each of them has a different job, too, cutting out the patterns, basting, sewing, stuffing. These jobs are changed now and then, so no one gets bored. Even the "cutters" seem pleased when they see the finished product.

There have been several of them who after a while shifted to the other table and actually made the dolls.

One final illustration might be cited of the kind of work that was done by the Ladies of the Long Table, as the ward staff dubbed them. The project under consideration was the making of decorated jars and bottles. In Step 1 a patient would sort different colored paper strips into piles of the same color. In the next step two patients sat opposite each other, across the table. One of them had a hand drill, to which a paper strip was attached. The second patient held the other end of the strip while her companion turned the drill, rolling the strip into a cord. When each cord was finished they exchanged jobs. Then two patients took the cord and wrapped it tightly around a glass jar. Two more patients glued the strip on, two more varnished the jars, and one checked the finished product for flaws. The completed jar was used for a vase or other decorative purposes on the ward, or as a gift for a patient at a ward party.

Some idea of the manner in which individual patients progressed through different stages in "cafeteria training" came from an interview the observer had with an aide who had been on the staff of B-1 from the beginning of the remotivation program. The following comments are again a reconstruction of the interview rather than a direct quotation.

When we started we sort of had to feel our way along. I started with ten patients at a time when I was asked if I would like to try my hand at doing things with patients. The chief nurse told us we could and that it would make our work with patients more interesting and easier in the long run. When I think back it did so all right.

At first I just tried making old string rugs to get the patients' fingers moving. The big problem was to keep the patients interested long enough. I started some of them with tearing and rolling the string into a ball. After a while, about six weeks or so, I started them on long wooden frames that some other patients in the receiving building had built. We used waxed string and the operation was simple. The patients could do counting, "under—over," "under—over," and that got them going. Sometimes we used strips of old bed sheets that other patients had made, and turned them into bath mats for the showers.

Then I started reed weaving. First we did potholder weaving, and when we mastered that we tried basket weaving. Then we did leather work and now a year and a quarter after I started, they're really quite artistic. I let them do copper work; some like chair weaving better. All the stuff they make goes to make the ward look nicer and some of the smaller things they can take with them when they are furloughed or transferred to a better ward. I try to let the patients pick what they like, once they get an idea of what they can do.

Since I started this I guess we've furloughed about six patients a year of the twenty-five or so patients I get a year, although I won't say they are restored to what they really were, but they were good enough to go back home. About another six of this group get promoted to a more advanced ward, where they have more ground privileges and do more shop work off the ward. Another half dozen or so I send to another ward that's similar to mine and we do that just because I think a change, even if they're not ready for promotion, does them good. The rest stay on a bit. Most of them will never make it and they get transferred to a custodial ward for a while and then they are put through again. Actually, most of them make good ward workers and some have become good in hospital industry, while before they did nothing but warm the benches and maybe weren't housebroken. So you see, the patients that once were untidy, even if they don't go home, become better adjusted. That's some gain anyway.

The effect of the habit training and "cafeteria training" on an individual patient is rather graphically portrayed in the following case history which was described to the observer by the charge nurse for B-2. Janie, as she was called, was quite a problem. She had been in the hospital for eighteen years without deriving any benefit from the somatic therapies. She had hallucinations but was mute except for occasions when she would have a violent outburst. She hoarded things, even chewed and ate string, and was really dirty and urinated in the corners. She was transferred to B-2 and put through the routine of habit training, much as has been described above. The charge nurse commented that once she got started she improved quite rapidly, and at the time of interview she was taking more interest in her appearance, not hoarding any more or "acting up." She learned to make attractive string dolls and do errands for the ward staff, with the prospect of soon being transferred to a better ward with a regular occupational therapy room. It was a source of much satisfaction to the charge nurse that she had disproved the remarks often made about Janie's not being suitable for occupational therapy— remarks that had been made previously about other patients. Her final comment was as follows: "We try things out as we think of them and if they work, good; if not, we find other ways of getting to the patients. I've learned a lot. I no longer try to rush patients, and I don't try to fit the patient to what she ought to do but what she can do comfortably."

The Daily and Weekly Routine

Perhaps a good way to summarize this material on habit training and "cafeteria training" is to outline the daily and weekly routine on B-1 and B-2 at the time of visit in April, 1954. The reader will remember that this was about fifteen months after the ward patient survey by the First Assistant Head Nurse and twenty-four months after the original transfer of regressed patients from the A area to the B wards.

The first two hours of the morning, from 7:30 to 9:30, were devoted to washing and grooming. This consisted of training in putting on shoes, brushing teeth, washing face, hands, arms, and other areas of the body, putting on clean clothing, combing hair, and applying lipstick and powder (for those who liked cosmetics). The basic principle utilized in carrying out this routine was that the patient do these things for herself, regardless of the time involved. If she was not able to do some or all of them for herself, the aides tried to teach her. The process was repeated day after day in the same way so that a habit pattern could be set up.

From 9:30 to 10:40 there were long-table activities: sewing, coloring, pulling burlap, cutting out pictures, putting puzzles together, stringing beads or macaroni, looking at magazines, listening to the radio, and so forth. There were group activities in the form of games, like Farmer in the Dell, or Ring Around the Rosy, marching to music, dancing, throwing the bean bag or ball, and various kinds of physical exercise.

Preparation for lunch began at a quarter to eleven. The tables were cleared and the patients helped in the lunch preparation by filling cups or soup bowls and carrying platters and dishes. Each aide tried to get several of her patients to help at this time even if it meant placing the platter in the patient's hands and guiding her to the table where she was to put the platter. After the tables had been set, each aide seated her patients at the table assigned to her, and only one aide seated her patients at a time. The object was to help the patients become accustomed to sitting at the same table each day with the same aide. It contributed to the feeling of belonging somewhere with someone.

Following lunch the patients washed and went to the toilet (for the incontinent patients toilet training was carried out every hour). From 1:30 until 3:15 there was more long-table retraining, and at 3:30 the preparation for supper began. When weather permitted there was a period of exercise outdoors, walking or playing simple games.

Weekly activities consisted of the following events. Tuesday and Friday were shower days, with each aide supervising her own group of patients. Monday morning was reserved for recorded music and guided activities like marching, dancing, and various games, under the direction of the music therapist and the occupational therapy aides. Wednesday afternoon was devoted to a strictly feminine institution, the beauty parlor. At the very beginning of the habit training program this period on Wednesday had to be devoted to basic scalp treatment in order to counteract the neglect engendered by long residence on the "untidy" wards. Later, the time was spent on shampoos, wave sets, permanents, and the varied activities of the beauty parlor that are a delight to women. It is interesting at this point to note that the staff originally used soft music to cut down excessive movement of patients. However, too many patients fell asleep on the chairs and benches. Boogie Woogie was then introduced, with some misgivings by the staff, but instead of disturbing the patients it provided the desired atmosphere. With improvement in the physical and social aspects of the patients the beauty shop hour was put on a biweekly basis, and alternated with a record hop, to which male patients were invited. Finally, there were movies every other Friday afternoon.

The observer was told that plans for the near future included the use of the hospital orchestra and chorus for ward entertainment on special occasions. At Christmas, or on important holidays, it was felt that patients could be further activated by this contact with social forces other than those directly connected with the ward.

Summary

Up to this point in our description of St. Charles Hospital we have tried to show how the pressure of a large number of chronic, seriously disturbed patients led to efforts at basic habit training, made possible in part by the remodeling of certain hospital wards, and in part by the interest of the administrative personnel and cooperation of the ward staff. Success in the habit training program precipitated a minor crisis, in that many improved patients who were transferred to better wards failed to sustain their improvement, and had to be returned to the chronic wards. The outcome was a growing program of intensive patient care, not only in habit training but also in the improvement of skills in social interaction through group activities, such as long-table retraining or "cafeteria training." At the time of the Survey there was a tendency to shift the basic habit training procedures back to the A wards, which constituted the reservoir of regressed patients, and to utilize Wards B-1 and B-2 more for the improvement of skills in social interaction through group activities.

There were other wards, however, which were concerned with the social remotivation of patients, and the picture of St. Charles Hospital will not be complete without a description of activities on those wards. To that end we now turn our attention.

PREPARING FOR LIFE ON THE OUTSIDE

C-7, the Ward with the Rehabilitation-Recreation Room

As part of the remodeling at St. Charles Hospital, certain changes were made in the C building which had eventual significance for patient remotivation. We are interested in one ward in particular in this building and in the activities that centered around the room that had once been a dining room. During the remodeling, a large dining room was constructed in the C building for the common use of the majority of the patients housed there. Hence, the dining room on Ward C-7, which was large enough to accommodate 40 persons comfortably, was no longer necessary and could therefore be utilized for other activities. The staff soon came to refer to it as the "Rehabilitation-Recreation Room," for it was the center around which remotivation activities moved on the ward.

Ward C-7 was called a semi-open ward for women, meaning that many of the patients who lived there had privileges to go to other parts of the hospital or onto the grounds. These were not "blanket" privileges; that is, they were not extended to all patients at all times, as would be the case on an open ward, but were granted with permission of the ward staff. Most of the patients were therefore better adjusted than the women on B-1 or the wards in the A building. They were habit trained and expressed, to varying degrees, an ability to relate to other people in a meaningful way; that is, to talk with them and work with them cooperatively.

Much of the group work in the Rehabilitation-Recreation Room was done around the "cutting table," really a variation of what was called long-table retraining on B-1 and B-2. The name "cutting table" was used because one of the main activities consisted of cutting material and making stuffed animals for children, pin cushions, and sofa pillows. The reader will remember that some cutting was done around the long table on B-1 and B-2, but it was a minor part of the activity program and only blunt scissors were used. On C-7 the procedure was somewhat like this: one woman collected all the trimmings from the pieces cut for the animals or cushions, then cut the trimmings into pieces as small as possible for stuffing. The advantage of this stuffing was that it would never pack or wad like cotton batting, and would loosen up with a little shaking. Colored cuttings were used mainly to stuff the pillows and cushions, white cuttings for the animals, for it was found that some mothers preferred white stuffing for children's toys. The finished products were then sold to visitors, friends, or volunteers to use as gifts for their own children or friends. Thus, the patients knew that their work was being appreciated; also they saw tangible results in the continued large size of the Patient Benefit Fund.

Other activities around the table included crocheting and sewing, making decorations for the walls and for special parties. One group, for example, might sew buttons together one day to make checkers for one of the wards in another building; a different group might sew together cloth samples from a store to make bedspreads for themselves.

Every day there were activities such as dancing, ball playing, or walks for patients on the grounds, weather permitting. Music was frequently played, on the piano or record player, fast and slow music being interspersed for the patient's moods. When playing ball, jazz seemed to be just the thing. Every week there was a record hop, to which male patients were invited, and to prevent "wall flowers" at these functions the ward staff and nursing students rotated around the dance floor.

Success of remotivation on C-7 was due in large measure to the use of the aides and to the fact that nursing students were assigned there for training. Each aide was assigned to a particular group of patients, usually 10 or 12 but sometimes more. Each group was mixed, in that some patients were easily handled, others were not, and members of each group followed the same activity at the same time. The aides seemed to like this plan, as seen in the comments one of them made to the observer.

> I like this group business; patients get to know me better and I them. . . . I think things really changed around here when attendants started doing things with patients. It took us a while to be confident. We just thought we were sort of guards for so long, but now we like our work real well and we can see patients get better. Each of us also has a special relief attendant who knows what we've been doing with our group of patients, so no trouble comes from this any more.

Originally, the students were assigned to C-7 so that they could have a better understanding of patients' needs as these related to a daily activity program. In addition to working with groups of patients, and participating in recreational activities, they were assigned to special patients. One of their activities with these special patients was reading sessions, for many of the women had really never learned to read well. As the charge nurse put it, "You see, some have to be reeducated from scratch so they can appreciate what to do with their leisure time when they move out of here."

In brief, the "cutting table," group activities with one aide, supervised recreation, activities with patients from other wards, and the experience of talking and working with the student nurses were the staples of the remotivation program on C-7.

D-1, the Occupational Therapy Room

Occupational therapy was as old as St. Charles itself, but this occupational therapy room differed from its predecessors, in that all patients from the open activity wards were free to participate. Previously, patients had been selected by the staff; now, they could walk in as they pleased. D-1, as we have called this particular occupational therapy room, was located in the new women's admission and intensive treatment building, and was directly adjacent to several ward areas. It was a big room, with many windows, a connecting bathroom, and supply closets. Any visitor could not fail to be struck by its attractiveness. Even the window ledges were always decorated with beautifully arranged flowers and potted plants. There were three sofas, a half-dozen cushioned chairs, many straight chairs, large tables, looms, rug frames, sewing machines, ironing board, piano, and an organ. One could not ask for better equipment.

Results of the activities in D-1 could be seen in the three show-cases. Here were cushions, tablecloths, potholders, scarfs, handkerchiefs, aprons, ceramics, stuffed animals, rugs, and many, many other useful articles which had been made by the women.

Individual patient experiences were less routinized than on the wards we have described at St. Charles Hospital. There was considerable freedom of choice of activities as well as more responsibility. Many of the patients who came to D-1 worked part time in hospital industries and helped to run the activities through a patient government organization. Although there were fewer staff members here, the patients experienced a wide range of interpersonal relationships. D-1 was used as a training area for nursing students and was a major anchor for the volunteer program at the hospital. The patients were therefore able to have more contact with people from the outside world and thus prepare themselves for eventual discharge. Both recreational and occupational activities were directed toward the same end, resumption of life in the community, and organizing a party, doing things for another group of patients, or making plans for ward activities, all gave experience in normal social skills.

PATIENT MOVEMENT

A look at Figure 2, on page 153, will show the informal treatment chain that existed at St. Charles Hospital. It was informal because few members of the staff saw movement from the A wards to B-1 and B-2 to C-7 to D-1 as a continuous process or succession of logical steps that a given patient might take toward recovery. In addition, some patients were transferred from any one of these wards to a domiciliary type of ward with less organized activity but more hospital industry, gardening, and occupational therapy. Direct discharges to the community had also taken place from each ward in the informal treatment chain.

At the time of the Survey visit there was a growing awareness of the possibilities of patient movement successively through these wards, each with its emphasis on a certain aspect of patient behavior and skills. Some of the staff were beginning to view this as a logical development of the long-term rehabilitation process. That they did not see it sooner was due in part to the fact that remotivation programs on the various wards grew slowly, out of need and interest rather than through systematic planning in advance, and in part to the fact that the staff were not psychologically prepared for a change in thinking to this extent.

COMMENTS AND CONCLUSIONS

The most important comment is an outgrowth of the remarks in the previous section and the initial experience in the habit

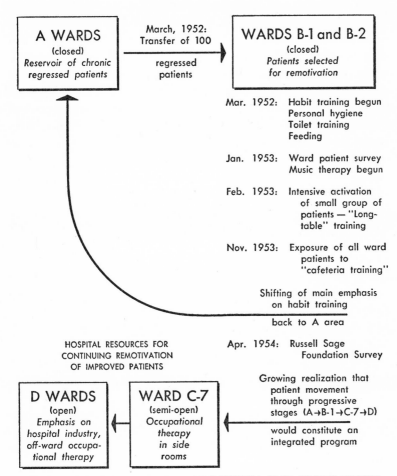

FIGURE 2. SEQUENCE OF EVENTS IN REMOTIVATION AT ST. CHARLES HOSPITAL

training program. The reader will remember that many patients who improved under habit training and were transferred to better wards soon lost their gains and had to be returned to the habit training ward. For the social remotivation of patients to be successful in the broadest sense; that is, for it to be effective for the greatest number of patients, it must be geared to different levels of patient adjustment and skills. When the seriously disturbed and incontinent patient has learned continence and cleanliness, he needs to go to an environment where there will be reenforcement of the new skills, as well as training in the elements of cooperation and group behavior. The ward personnel of the new ward must be prepared to accept his limitations, to take him as he is and support him, meanwhile directing his energies in new areas of social interaction. Staff on semi-open rehabilitation wards must not forget that some patients may find the new responsibilities overpowering, and must be prepared to help the patient by providing some staff member with whom he can form a close, supportive relationship which will carry him through this painful period. In short, a conscious recognition of the steps in remotivation, all the way from marked regression to discharge, must be kept in mind and incorporated into total effort. St. Charles Hospital had all the basic ingredients for a total program. There was interest on the part of both the administration and the aides; there was a successful habit training program in operation which was being extended to all the "untidy" wards; there was the assignment of one aide to a specific group of patients; there was an integration of occupational and recreational therapy work with basic nursing care right on the wards.

That a total program had not been devised was due in no small measure to the fact that overall, or long-term rehabilitation programs in state hospitals represent a change in traditional ways of thinking. Staff members have for so long been burdened with immediate ward problems that they have not been able to look beyond their own wards. Indeed, where the Legend of Chronicity has operated, staff had no reason to make long-range plans for their patients. However, with new approaches to patient care, with the utilization of social remotivation, mental hospital personnel can legitimately expect the necessity for devising a program that provides for the movement of the patient through a series of ward environments with ever-increasing social responsibilities. The staff at St. Charles had not yet fully adopted the frame of reference of an integrated program, yet all evidence indicated that it was soon to come.

8. Social Self-Renewal and Community Volunteers

THE SUCCESSFUL TREATMENT OF PATIENTS with mental disease cannot be divorced from the interest and activities of people in the general community. This is true for two reasons. In the first place, the social adjustment of the discharged patient depends in large measure on the attitudes and actions of family, friends, and others in the community. Whatever beneficial effects have been rendered by the hospital can be undone quickly by rejecting or fearful people, or they can be reinforced and extended by acceptance and interest. The reintegration of the ill person into normal society can thus be thought of as an extension of the treatment process.

In the second place, the ability of the hospital to provide adequate care and treatment for those residing within its walls is intimately related to the recognition by people in the community of the need for both their legislative and moral support. When the mental hospital and its patients are pushed out of sight and out of mind by the ordinary citizen, it is difficult for elected representatives and administrative officials to pay much attention to requests for adequate budgets and competent staffs. The history of neglect in our public mental institutions is tragic evidence of the truth of this idea.

Mobilization of the extra hospital world, therefore, can be considered logically both a direct and indirect factor in the remotivation of patients. As such it is pertinent to the purpose of this book; indeed, it is necessary for a complete picture of encouraging efforts in the remotivation of mental patients.

An excellent example of one way in which involvement of people outside the hospital may be brought about is through a program of ward visiting by volunteers from the community. The volunteer movement has direct remotivational features to the extent that the visitors bring some of the "outside" into the patient world, enough so that many patients are encouraged to reestablish some of their channels of interpersonal relationships and interests in the activities of others. It has somewhat more indirect remotivational features to the extent that it changes attitudes in the community toward the mental patient, making him feel less conspicuous when he goes out "on visit" and less rejected when he is discharged. Furthermore, the volunteer movement may have important side influences on legislative programs, to say nothing of the value for the individual participant in giving himself emotionally to a worthwhile cause. This chapter describes the growth of a volunteer movement in a southern town, where these features were indeed realized and the remotivation of patients was greatly facilitated.

Central State Hospital, located on the outskirts of Doville, a town of about 6,000 people, and across the river from Sandria, a small southern city of over 50,000, is a mental institution caring for some 2,900 patients. Twenty-five years ago the superintendent stated in his biennial report to the Board of Administrators that it should never be allowed to have more than 1,500 patients.

Like many similar institutions, Central State Hospital is a community within itself. It has a dairy, bakery, laundry, butcher shop, canteen, cannery, shoeshop, barber shop, broom shop, sewing and mending room, greenhouse, farms, and recreational center.

At the time of the Survey in May of 1954, somewhat more than 1,000 patients were living in four buildings that were constructed between 1902 and 1907. These three-story buildings had brick walls with wooden inner structures which had deteriorated to the point of being almost beyond repair. Only patching and repatching for the past twenty years had prevented their complete breakdown. Their toilet facilities, especially, were inadequate and outmoded.

These buildings housed the average type of state hospital patient, with four very disturbed wards and two incontinent wards where many old and debilitated patients were to be found. In one of the buildings there were more than 300 white women, divided into floors of residence according to the severity of their condition. Two open wards were located on the first floor where 70-odd patients were allowed freedom to come and go on the hospital grounds. The two locked wards on the second floor were occupied by 135 mildly disturbed patients, while on the third floor 110 highly disturbed or "untidy" patients were housed in two locked wards. As a rule, the limited ward staff found it difficult to manage these patients, necessitating the occasional use of some form of wrist restraint to prevent them from harming themselves or others. Frequently, there was only one attendant and never more than three on a ward.

The rest of the patients were housed in newer buildings. Even here the wards were in need of major repairs, with the exception of one new building for reception and intensive treatment of female patients. This meant that by necessity rather than choice the hospital had to have large maintenance crews. Even so, repairs in the institution were about ten years behind schedule.

The sewer system was completely inadequate and deteriorated, with one of the hospital lines emptying into one of the lines of the town of Doville. This line frequently ruptured and overflowed into a low area within the town limits, bringing numerous complaints. For many years this odor was an oft-talked-about symbol of disrespect for the hospital itself.

The medical staff was limited both in number of physicians and nursing personnel. With only six physicians there was a patient quota of more than 490 per man, and each of them was responsible for the physical care of patients as well as their mental treatment. There were only 11 registered nurses in the institution, who were limited to work as supervisors or on wards in the female patient section or the medical and surgical building. The 226 aides were evenly divided between the male and female sections.

At the time of visit, occupational therapy was available for some of the white women patients and a smaller number of the white men patients. Except for the men's occupational shop, the activities were conducted by nurses and specially trained aides on the wards or in large rooms connected with the wards.

Most of the Negro patients and the majority of white men patients who did not work in some hospital industry or go to the occupational shop spent their days in closed wards just sitting on the floor or hard benches. Their main form of recreation was an occasional movie shown on the ward. As a rule, they were not allowed to attend church in the low-ceilinged wooden recreational building. The softball games and other sports events were not on their schedule because there were insufficient attendants to supervise them while they were outside. Their only "comforts" were their narrow white cots, which occupied most of the space on the wards, and a few hard chairs. At one end of each ward were some crude wooden tables and benches where the meals were served.

Instead of being tempting, their food was often unappetizing and cold. Before the macaroni, red beans and sausage, corn bread and milk could reach the scattered tin plates and cups at the table where the closed-ward patient sat, it had to be brought by a bucket brigade of open-ward patients from the main kitchen some distance away. The open-ward patients ate in the main dining room, but this was located in a building wing that had been declared unsafe inasmuch as its foundations were sinking and the walls cracked both inside and out.

This institution presented a grim picture of adverse conditions for patient care, the kind calculated to dampen the initiative of even the most enthusiastic worker. Yet, contrary to expectations, the hospital staff exhibited high spirits and much resourcefulness in the performance of the daily routine. Their strength and pride seemed to stem from two major sources. One was a well-accepted and effective volunteer program; the other was the fact that owing to widespread public pressure some of the deplorable physical conditions were about to be eliminated with the help of newly granted state building funds.

There was also a third reason for the high staff morale. The observer was told repeatedly that in the past two years, and especially since the more widespread use of volunteers, the percentage of patient turnover had noticeably increased, and the length of stay for first admissions had been reduced.

The air of optimism about the future was coupled with a sense of past achievement. A patient library, even though not yet adequate, was functioning where there was none previously. More patients had grounds privileges than ever before, a hospital chapel was under construction, foundations for new receiving and treatment buildings had been laid, and a salary increase was in the offing.

The Beginnings of a Volunteer Movement

A more startling contrast between a largely antiquated hospital plant and severe personnel shortages on the one hand, and high staff morale, sense of purpose, and active community interest on the other is hard to find. Actually it all began almost by accident sometime in 1952. The Musical Club of Doville, through its president, Mrs. Markham, received an invitation from Dr. Schroder, the superintendent of Central State Hospital, to bring its music to the institution. The invitation was unexpected. The townspeople did not recall that anyone at the state hospital had ever tried anything comparable to this before. Mrs. Markham and her friends considered the request, knowing from their experience at a Veterans Administration hospital that there would be value in music for the healing of the mentally ill. She decided to discuss it further with Dr. Schroder, with whom she was well acquainted socially, for he and his family lived outside the institution and had during the past few years mingled freely with the townspeople. She knew, therefore, that he must have given the request careful thought and had weighed the aloof attitude of the town toward the hospital. In the course of their discussion she suggested a further approach: why not help the patients form their own chorus? Dr. Schroder was especially pleased with this idea, and appointed Dr. Hansen, the chief psychologist and Mrs. Bates, the chief social worker, to prepare the hospital staff for the initiation of a choral project.

With the assistance of the Reverend Mr. Morris of neighboring Sandria, Mrs. Markham gathered a small group of patients and began to hold weekly rehearsals in the hospital recreation hall. As one might expect, there were difficulties. Many of the patients came at first more out of curiosity than because of their vocal ability. Also, there was the problem of noise interference, for while the chorus was practicing at one end of the room other patients were playing pool at the opposite end. In spite of these drawbacks both the patients and hospital staff seemed interested in the project and appreciative of the efforts in their behalf.

At about this time another event occurred that was to assume importance in the development of the volunteer organization. This was the observation of National Hospital Day. The hospital staff prepared for openhouse, but only six people came, two of whom were from out of town. Mrs. Markham, who was conducting the patient chorus that day, suddenly realized the extent to which the hospital was rejected by the town. However, those at C.S.H. were not surprised; they cited records to show that one patient had not had a friend or relative visit him during his twenty-six years at the hospital. The town, indeed, had been aloof from the hospital. Mrs. Markham recalled later that "faced with such a small attendance at openhouse something had to be done." The result was a determination on her part to stimulate community interest in this institution of forgotten people.

Meanwhile, news of the patient chorus spread through the hospital grounds and beyond. The local newspaper brought out news releases of the Musical Club activities at the hospital in its regular local news column. As more patients joined the group the caliber of the singing improved. Some invitations were even received to sing at churches in the Sandria and Doville area, happenings without precedent. During the months following, through the friendship of the assistant manager of a local radion station, tape recordings of the chorus were made for local broadcast. Occasionally they were even broadcast on a statewide basis.

The request for the Musical Club to come to the hospital and Mrs. Markham's reaction to a hospital devoid of visitors on National Hospital Day were the key starting points in community interest in the hospital. Had it not been for this lady, with her high social prestige and her strategically placed friends in the community, to say nothing of her initiative, things might have been quite different.

Two other events occurred during the summer that helped to prepare the way for the beginning of a volunteer group. The first of these was a party, late in August, which was given jointly by patients and the occupational therapy department in honor of Mrs. Markham and a newspaper friend, Mrs. Harrison. It was held on one of the wards in the women's admission building and was featured by gifts for the two honored guests, which had been made for them by the patients. Several members of the Musical Club and their friends from Sandria and Doville participated, as did Dr. Schroder and many invited staff members from other wards. This did much to cement better hospital-community relations.

The other event was the initiation of a hospital newspaper, which greatly facilitated the dissemination of news among hospital staff and patients. This monthly journal was launched with the help of several patient reporters from different buildings and the encouragement of the psychology department. As will be seen later, it contributed in no small measure to the acceptance of the volunteer program.

On August 31, 1952, the first formal meeting to discuss the possibility of a volunteer program was held at Mrs. Markham's home in Doville. Dr. Schroder, Dr. Hansen, and Mrs. Bates represented the hospital, and representatives from 10 churches and 18 civic and fraternal organizations in Sandria and Doville were present.

In terms of general principles all agreed that hospital volunteers should be drawn from all religious faiths and from all the organizational groups in the two communities. It should not be an exclusive movement. Furthermore, the purpose of a group of volunteers should be twofold: to use the social resources of the community for the rehabilitation of patients and to familiarize the public with the overall hospital program. Volunteers could help patients by bringing some of the outside world into the hospital, providing "little extras" that they would not ordinarily have, and supplying a home atmosphere for an otherwise drab institutional setting. It was understood that volunteers would not be expected to perform the duties of hospital personnel but could arouse new avenues of interest in the patients for which regular hospital personnel did not have the time or the talent.

The group then discussed ways in which some of these general ideas might be implemented in their particular community situation. It was felt the volunteers could be effective in urging many of the musically inclined and artistically accomplished patients to perform for other patients. The Musical Club could be especially valuable in this direction. Furthermore, it was deemed feasible for classes of church schools, women's church groups, and civic clubs, to consider some kind of project at the hospital for the coming year, in accordance with the general aim of bringing some of the outside world into the wards. To further this idea it was suggested that each person in attendance discuss the matter with his particular church or club and seek to stimulate interest there.

Two organizational steps were taken: first, the formation of a Hospital Advisory Committee, which would inquire into patient needs, and formulate both immediate and long-range objectives for the volunteers; second, the selection of a Survey Committee which would study volunteer groups operating in other institutions. Together the committees would consider the practical problems of forms of suitable entertainment, development of patient and volunteer talent, and ways of ward visitation. They would also consider the present and potential facilities of the hospital which might be made available to the volunteers.

The meeting concluded on a most encouraging note, brought about by the spontaneous remark of a member of the Exchange Club. He said that he had lived in Sandria for forty-seven years and had never once been inside the hospital. Feeling that it was time for a change, he invited a member of the hospital staff to address a meeting of his club, for projects like the volunteer movement were in line with the covenant of the club. Other club representatives quickly followed his lead in asking the hospital staff to give orientation talks to their organizations and another step was taken in the improvement of hospital-community relations.

Formation of the Patient Service Organization

On September 15, 1952, more than 125 representatives of all faiths and civic clubs in the two communities met at the Sandria Community Center to organize the Patient Service Organization, which soon came to be known as the P.S.O. Dr. Schroder and Dr. Hansen from the hospital opened the meeting by telling those present about hospital life, and especially the role that volunteers might play in breaking down the barriers for patients who had become involved in the institutional way of life and introducing them once again to the realities of the world outside.

After a question and answer period the group came to agreement on the kinds of volunteers needed, noting that both men and women should be included in the organization, inasmuch as patient status was no respecter of sex. First would be the individual willing to visit patients in a ward setting. This type of volunteer, because of his particular skills and experience, would be qualified to lead patients in educational or recreational activities. Also, this category included those who would organize arts and crafts classes, hold religious meetings, organize music programs, and work on various projects that might be planned for holidays or other special occasions. The second type of volunteer would direct his activities toward the club, church class, or other group to which he belonged. This role would involve providing the necessary resources for giving parties or other programs for the patients and lending support in any way possible to community aspects of P.S.O. projects. Implicit in the role of the second type of volunteer was the necessity for keeping himself informed about the work of the mental hospital and of passing this information on to others.

It is important to note that the need for this second type of volunteer category was stressed from the beginning by those who participated in the original planning. They were convinced of the need for a broad base of community support, and realized that it would be necessary to make a special appeal to those who like to give and want to be charitable but hesitate to mingle with the mentally ill. It was hoped that they would get as much out of the activities of the organization as those who were to work with patients directly.

A note of reassurance was interjected into the meeting through an announcement by Dr. Hansen that a volunteer orientation course and tours through the hospital had been scheduled for each Tuesday and Thursday during the coming month. For those unable to attend at these hours special tours were to be arranged for nights and on Sunday. The purpose of these tours was in part to relieve natural anxieties about mental illness, as well as to acquaint prospective volunteer workers with the best methods for meeting patient needs.

Dr. Hansen followed his first announcement with another well-timed statement, to the effect that the first organization to begin functioning in the new organization was the Lions Club of Doville. Under their auspices a box had been placed at the Doville fire station on Main Street where books and magazines could be deposited for the hospital's library. There was a round of expressions of approval and indications that those present would see to it that the box would never be empty.

Colonel Gates, influential Sandria citizen and member of the Hospital Advisory Committee then spoke: "There's another need, too. In the occupational therapy ward the patients are often idle for lack of materials for making articles that would fill their empty hours. When I inquired why these things weren't supplied, the answer was that the state budget doesn't include all the little extras." Many of those at the meeting were surprised to hear this but promised action in their respective clubs and church groups.

A digression is necessary here to discuss this problem pertaining to economic support, which is usually acute in state hospitals. There is no money in the budget for extras and as a rule occupational therapy is put on a production and self-support basis. For the same reason, the hospital sewing and mending room is often classified as an occupational therapy activity. In reality, the working conditions and lack of gratifications are frequently distressing. Since the general public is seldom aware of the problem, it is noteworthy that it was brought out at this meeting and interpreted as a call for community action.

The meeting concluded with the appointment of a nominating committee, consisting of members of the Hospital Advisory Committee, which would bring in a slate of officers to be elected at a meeting on October 13. Also at that meeting representatives of each organization were asked to report on ways in which their particular group would participate in the volunteer activities. Between these two meetings they were charged with the responsibility of carrying back to their clubs a full report of the evening's proceedings, with special emphasis on the aims and roles of the volunteers. Full newspaper coverage of the proceedings was also planned, so that no channels of vital communication were left to chance.

At this point in the presentation of organizational developments two other pieces of information are pertinent. The first relates to the election of officers and the appointment of permanent committees. It was hoped that with a strong line organization the administrative system would be efficient. There were some volunteers, however, who felt that only future events could indicate the need for extensive organization in the volunteer movement. They reasoned, and Mrs. Markham was among them, that the autonomy of individual desires to help could be jeopardized by too much centralization of function. Such foresight is suggestive of the real ability of the volunteer leaders.

Second, the degree of thoroughness in the preparation for the launching of the volunteer movement is noteworthy. The deft coordination and timing of both thought and action between the hospital staff and the community representatives contributed to the relative ease of establishing certain ground rules about volunteer work. This was aided in part by the fact that both the hospital and community seemed ready for each other and awoke to this realization at about the same time, and in part by the lack of haste or improvisation by the volunteer leaders.

At the same time, Dr. Schroder and Dr. Hansen initiated a training program at the hospital with a personal orientation to all ward staff about the use of volunteers. They believed it desirable to build up substantial staff interest before the formal organization of the volunteers took place. Their motive was to keep conscious frustration among hospital workers to a minimum and thereby preclude an outburst of negativism when the volunteers began to arrive in numbers.

Through the orientation program they became aware that occupational and recreational therapy workers showed more resistance to the idea of volunteers than did the nurses and aides. They seemed to feel that their skills were too specialized to permit the introduction, or really the intrusion, of outsiders. Thus, it was decided that the main volunteer effort would be directed at first through the nursing department and the wards. On more reflection there seemed to be other advantages to this plan. Contact with patients through occupational therapy or recreational therapy might be too intermittent and the volunteer might become too content with this mode of contact and hesitant about branching out onto the wards. Since this was all decided before the organizational meeting was held, the hospital saved the volunteers from a possible early setback.

The Growing Volunteer Program

Once the formal organization of the P.S.O. was completed, the volunteer program quickly picked up speed, as manifested in the number of varied ward visitation activities and of recreational and educational programs. To give a full picture here of these would be impossible; instead, we have selected a number at random which reflect the effect of the program on hospital life.

Thanksgiving Day celebrations at the hospital, sponsored by the P.S.O., were an excellent example of this new volunteer effort. A newspaper report written by Mrs. Harrison, carried the following item:

> Family groups throughout the nation will gather to share their gifts and the proverbial turkey. But for some there'll be no going home. The measure of their joy will depend on the generosity of

others. In this group belong the hospitalized mental patients. Those at the Central State Hospital have fared far better, and will do so at Yule time, than patients in many other hospitals, for our townspeople are beginning to realize the field of service open to the volunteer worker at such institutions.

This quotation not only gives some idea of the effect of the Thanksgiving efforts, but points as well to the manner in which news of the volunteer effort was disseminated to the community. The importance of generous newspaper support cannot be underestimated in making the volunteer movement a success. Much of the credit for the strong response of the local community to the call for volunteers must go to this staff writer and friend of the hospital, Mrs. Harrison. In many ways she succeeded in making P.S.O. work not only a series of important community social events but also an enjoyable form of welfare activity.

As a result of the P.S.O. interest a great amount of material support began for the patients. For example, a church group from a neighboring town became one of the largest contributors of money, books, and clothing for patients. Because of these many gifts and the more favorable community attitude engendered by the volunteers, a greater number of patients began to attend church in the community. The local newspaper reported this succinctly.

Volunteer gifts of normal wearing apparel enabled a patient to be inconspicuous at church. No longer did he have to feel self-conscious and stared at as a museum piece. Without these gifts patients would have to continue to wear their blue jeans and jumpers.

Since many townspeople had come to associate mental patients with ill-fitting, state-supplied clothing, and had often commented on the fact that you cannot be seen with them outside the hospital, the P.S.O. clothing program was, indeed, a vital first step toward achieving community acceptance. By thus removing a symbol of disrespect for the hospital, many P.S.O. members were able subsequently to convince reluctant townspeople that mental patients were not necessarily people who have to be locked up. Instead, they could point with pride to those patients who had freely mingled with them when they went to church.

Religious life within the hospital was not neglected either. Each Sunday the rector of the Doville Episcopal Church held a morning worship service at the hospital. Similarly, two members of the Doville Baptist Church conducted a Sunday school class for a large ward of senile patients. Not content with spiritual efforts alone, they initiated a joint patient-aide ward redecoration project. This was much needed, for the ward was located in one of the four oldest buildings on the grounds.

Musical and recreational events also received emphasis. The patient choir, which Mrs. Markham had organized, joined with the Musical Club to present recitals in the Methodist churches of Sandria and Doville. This was so successful that invitations were soon received from other churches. Under the direction of some members of the Musical Club, the patient chorus gave many concerts for patients on the wards. A music appreciation class was begun, and a member of the Sandria Methodist Church group started weekly piano lessons. Before long she had six regular patient students.

Two weeks before Christmas, a group of students from a local college staged a full dress rehearsal of a Broadway stage hit at the hospital. During the following week the Doville Lions Club gave a rehearsal performance of its yearly minstrel show. In addition, a patient-volunteer program of folk dancing was held every Thursday on the white women's convalescent ward.

After the beginning of the new year a great effort was made to extend the volunteer program to the Negro section of the hospital. No one underestimated the problem of overcoming racial barriers and a slow response at first was expected. However, Mrs. Markham, by being the first to establish contact with members of a Negro congregation, set a decisive example for other white P.S.O. members to follow. As in the original development of volunteer activities, the first effort was made with music, and a Negro patient choir performed for a mixed audience, including both Negro and white patients and townspeople, in the hospital recreation hall. From here it was not too difficult to expand P.S.O. activities gradually into some of the better Negro wards and later on into other wards.

Changes at the First Level of Achievement

The high level of community interest and activities at the hospital which built up during the fall and winter inevitably ran into some dangers, especially a slackening of the pace of volunteer effort. At one of their teas certain influential volunteer members overheard others objecting to proposals for new activities, inasmuch as they believed that already they were doing enough. This sign of danger was acted on quickly with a review of activities by hospital staff and key members of the P.S.O.

One important source of danger which became apparent from the review was the practice of ward adoptions by various member organizations of the P.S.O. Initially, it was felt that this practice would increase community enthusiasm, which in fact it did, and both the hospital staff and community leaders had been in favor of such a policy. As time wore on, they realized that among some local clubs ward adoption was fulfilling a negative need when the clubs exerted efforts to turn particular wards into their private preserves. Their reluctance to let other clubs bring programs into these wards meant that they had put up mental "no trespassing" signs. The hospital staff knew that this practice could lead to entertainment doldrums and could make for serious rifts among the patients and ward personnel. For the same reason there was danger in the adoption of veteran patients on various wards. Dr. Hansen echoed the feelings of the staff about this when he said, "They're as ill as the others; mental illness knows no privileged persons."

This situation is a good example of how an initially good need may turn into a harmful one in the long run, a danger which faces all volunteer movements and which can only be overcome by a flexibility of thought and willingness to pursue a serious review of work.

Consequently a decision was made to institute a ward rotation plan whereby each ward would be covered by different organizations from time to time. As a result, many volunteers again felt freer to do what they wanted for and with the patients. Also, this decision was made at a time when many volunteers felt they had matured sufficiently to be able to handle work in more disturbed wards. Thus, if the ward adoption system had been retained, fewer volunteers would have decided to try to help the more difficult patients.

In conjunction with the adoption of the ward rotation plan came the realization that a better volunteer orientation program was needed, especially for those who wished to work on the disturbed wards. This led to plans for an elective ten-hour orientation course in addition to the informal talks and hospital tours. The course was scheduled for twice a year, in the fall and spring, allowing time for the new groups of volunteers to become adjusted before the next ones branched out to the locked wards.

At about this time an unwritten mode of operation was adopted. The hospital staff and volunteer leaders joined forces in subtly discouraging all persons whose desire to help seemed motivated mainly by the need for social prestige or "do-goodism." Although they were discouraged from working directly with patients, an earnest attempt was made to persuade them to become active organizational members in their own clubs. In spite of some resentment of this policy, the vast majority of P.S.O. members were well satisfied.

The organizational changes culminated during the summer of 1953 with the appointment of a volunteer coordinator, Mrs. Bates, the chief social worker. She had functioned as an outstanding informal adviser from the beginning of the movement; her immediate contacts in the community were numerous; and she was highly respected at the hospital for her judgment. Her selection was, therefore, an ideal one.

Her role as the integrator of hospital and volunteer services involved a number of responsibilities. It was her job to reconcile differences about time, date, and place of activities, to organize a record-keeping system, and to establish a central location in the administration building for volunteer equipment and supplies. In addition, she was to hold monthly inservice discussions with ward personnel to review current volunteer and staff problems and new patient needs.

Decentralization of the P.S.O.

With the task of integrating hospital and volunteer effort in the hands of Mrs. Bates many of the formal committees of the P.S.O. were no longer necessary, and were discontinued in September, 1953.

Mrs. Markham and others considered this decentralization most appropriate. Their view was that a formal constitution, many officers, and committees provide too many opportunities for time to be wasted on administrative maneuvering and unnecessary paper work. In addition, those at the top often might emphasize improperly their loyalty to their own club or church group, or forget the real purpose of the volunteers. Mrs. Markham expressed herself in this fashion:

> We do just as we please. We found that designated committees, when we tried to make them formal, did not work out so well. It worked better just letting the volunteers from the different clubs work as they wanted to. When we have something to discuss, we call each other up and have a tea and talk things over. After all, the many clubs have P.S.O. as just one of their important functions.

Again, here was an awareness on the part of those responsible for the program of how originally good needs can lead eventually to bad ones; in this case an original emphasis on organizational details leading to possible misdirection of effort. Had the volunteer organization remained unchanged, it is probable that a leveling off, or even a deterioration of volunteer work and community response might have taken place. Indeed, when the hospital was visited in May of 1954, it was the observer's opinion that the change to autonomous functioning of the various P.S.O. affiliated clubs had contributed to the expansion of volunteer activities at the hospital.

The superintendent of the hospital in particular was pleased with this shift in emphasis, feeling that sterile programs of "canned joy" had been avoided by the organizational changes, especially in ward rotation and in decentralization. It seemed to him that many volunteers had begun to shift from the quantitative to the qualitative aspects of their work, being concerned less about the number of volunteers from each club and the number of hours spent in routine ward visitation. Instead, they discussed more often the different ways in which they could contribute their services to the individual needs of patients.

The Second Phase of Achievement, Under the Volunteer Coordinator

Much of the subsequent development of volunteer work at Central State Hospital depended on the action of the volunteer coordinator, Mrs. Bates. Though she had few precedents to follow, she attempted to find impartial answers to the varied problems, and did not hesitate to discard an apparent solution if it did not seem to be working. An example of her liaison between hospital personnel and volunteers was shown in her decision to have ward staff indicate the type of activities they felt most appropriate for particular patients, also to evaluate every month the volunteer programs on the wards. Both staff and volunteers appreciated this procedure, for they realized the necessity of an objective check on the direction of volunteer efforts.

Another illustration of Mrs. Bates' activity could be seen when cooperation from the recreational therapy department lagged despite much informal pressure. The volunteer coordinator then concentrated her effort in securing more cooperation in scheduling from the occupational therapy department and the nursing service. It was not hard to persuade occupational therapy to coordinate its efforts with those of the volunteers. The persuasive force of a continuous and large supply of raw materials from the P.S.O. was not to be denied. These materials included coat hangers, scrap lumber, books, clothing, old hats, map linen, flower bulbs and seeds, gift wrappings, and various woodworking materials. Especially appreciated were graded pieces of rags of many colors and weaves.

The cooperation of occupational therapy became even more willing when it became known that some volunteers had spent hours together to sort the rags and grade them. Indeed, the Lions Club rag collection was doing so well that some local rag pickers felt their business was threatened with extinction, which led them to complain to the Better Business Bureau in Sandria of unfair competition. Finally, an agreement was worked out whereby the volunteers sold only a small part of their graded rags to raise cash for ward projects, and donated the larger part to occupational therapy at the hospital.

Mrs. Bates knew that it would be a slow process to coordinate the regular recreational therapy program with volunteer efforts, especially when it became evident that recreational therapy had instituted a saturation program of activities on particular wards that made it difficult to find free time for volunteers. She therefore turned to Dr. Schroder, the superintendent, who, after noting that coordination had worked well in other departments, made two rules. First, any special volunteer program would have preference automatically over the regular recreational therapy programs. Second, any regular volunteer program, so designated by the physician or volunteer coordinator, would have conditional preference over recreational therapy. He asked the recreational therapy staff to consider that volunteer activities were a part of the normal patient day, and that it was desirable, therefore, to assist the volunteers in every way possible. With this decision overt resistance collapsed.

Covert resistance was only overcome as some of the more experienced volunteers began to draw one of the three recreational therapists into their activities on a consulting basis. The volunteers then began to notice that at those events where consultation had been deliberately sought the amount of ambulatory patient participation and enthusiasm increased considerably. They also began to realize that the experience of recreational therapy personnel was helpful to them in planning their activities. Thus, the way was opened for an eventual complete coordination of efforts between recreational therapy and volunteers, comparable to that experienced in other areas of the hospital program.

Sidelights of the Volunteer Undertaking

We have presented, in essence, the chronicle of events in the birth and growth of the volunteer movement at Central State

Hospital, up to the time of the Survey visit in May of 1954. It would not be complete, however, without a fuller description of various volunteer activities and innovations with the patients, for of such things excitement and enthusiasm are made.

Men often like to go fishing, but being a patient in a mental hospital rather precludes such a pastime, at least, in most places; however, not at Central State Hospital. The volunteers provided the supplies and the encouragement for making equipment, all the way from the flies to the rods, reels, and baskets. Ward personnel made it clear that this was a "manly" activity which would not only be fun but also help them get well. Indeed, it did. After a patient group had completed their equipment, they would go on a fishing party with the volunteers to the pond that was located on the hospital grounds. The outing was completed with an outdoor fish fry and group singing. The patient response was gratifying and the ward staff were pleased to see many patients who had previously been withdrawn now show an interest in social activity.

Cooking and pastry-making parties were initiated for women patients in a convalescent ward, with a ward kitchen the scene of operations. The cookies, sandwiches, or other food were then used as refreshments at a party of their own or at a surprise party for the volunteers.

Plans were under way to extend patient food preparation to the hospital canteen service, for the volunteers thought it desirable that the patients sell at least some of their products to other patients and visitors, and above all to the staff. The proceeds from such sale were to be turned over to a special patient fund for the ward redecoration projects which the volunteers had sponsored. The appropriateness of this plan and of the other projects as part of an overall effort to remotivate patients realistically cannot be denied.

Patient government was introduced on a limited scale in the women's convalescent and acute treatment building. The rudiments for a patient organization already existed there on an informal basis, for the patients themselves kept the building clean, did their own ironing, and prepared and served the food. With the advent of many volunteer-sponsored activities the need for further organization became evident. As a result, patients on this ward undertook to plan and present their own entertainment programs, given for guest patients from other wards. From here it was just a step to more self-discipline, patient initiative, and some self-government.

Volunteer stimulation was behind the formation of a patient rhythm band, which came to be known as the Roving Rhythm Band. Help was forthcoming from the occupational therapy department, enabling patients to make their own instruments from scrap lumber and other leftover materials, instruments such as tub-a-phones, frying pan banjos, and nail keg drums. Without very much practice it was possible to produce simple folk tunes, and the fact that the instruments were homemade meant that no one was apprehensive about his musical skill or about breaking them. The band provided a good many hours of fun for patients who seldom left the closed wards.

Still other volunteer activities were in promising stages of development at the time of the Survey in 1954. For example, visits of selected patients to Doville and Sandria homes had begun at the suggestion of Mrs. Markham, who had been the first to invite a patient from the hospital choir to her home. The potential value of the practice was illustrated in the case of a young woman with advanced degrees in music who had completely ignored her training since becoming a patient. Mrs. Markham invited her to her home each week for afternoon coffee and a visit. After they had become well acquainted, Mrs. Markham one day produced her cello and began to tune it; the young woman soon found herself at the piano, and gradually the long spell of withdrawal from music was broken. Although few cases would ever be as dramatic, the value of home visits was well recognized at the hospital, and the idea had progressed to the point where the volunteer coordinator was working out a regular home visit plan.

A hospital gardening program, especially for elderly patients, had been launched by the Doville Garden Club, appropriately enough at a special garden party.

One final but most important illustration remains to be given. A special effort was made to interest the widows and widowers of the community in the plight of the mental patient. Mrs. Markham pointed out that "if you get to them just a little before they all but retire to the rocker and lavish their affection and care on a pet, a cat or a dog, you will have the most enthusiastic and earnest workers for the P.S.O." Her common sense psychology was, indeed, validated by at least a dozen of these persons. In particular, they devoted themselves to the patients at such times when other volunteers were normally occupied with homemaking, professional, and business functions. They were especially welcome visitors to the wards on long holiday weekends when the other volunteers had family obligations and could not come.

Like the efforts of the volunteer coordinator, all these projects were characterized by the experimental outlook, by the willingness to try something new, to be unafraid of trial and error and of mistakes. As we have pointed out earlier, such an approach undoubtedly contributed to the success of overcoming the everpresent danger of reaching a plateau of therapeutic effort. In addition to the spirit behind the project was the result, a vital contribution to the overall hospital effort to remotivate patients realistically, to lead them to a better hospital adjustment, or to prepare them for resumption of regular life in society.

Unexpected Results

A volunteer program may have certain practical results that were not expected explicitly at the beginning. There were two consequences of this kind in the story of the Sandria and Doville volunteers, one related to the patients, one to politics.

When the six-month period, July to December, 1952, was compared with the same period a year later, it was found that the patient turnover rate changed from 68 per cent to 79 per cent. There was thus an 11 per cent increase in patient movement in one year. The superintendent attributed this increase largely to a more active treatment program, inspired by the community volunteers. The number of hospital personnel had not increased during this time.

The P.S.O. was recognized by the State Department of Mental Health when the Director of Mental Health on September 11, 1953, advocated adoption of the program in other state institutions. Furthermore, he recommended that before organizing their programs other institutions might study with much profit what had been done at Central State Hospital.

In 1954 the state legislature approved a bond issue, which listed over two and a half million dollars for the hospital. This meant that eight 66-patient dormitories could be constructed, which would permit moving to them about half the patients who were presently housed in the oldest buildings on the grounds. The importance of a well-run and influential P.S.O. can be seen if one notes that the bond issue in question was approved after the legislature had voted 40 millions for roads but could not make up its mind on the support for institutions. A letter campaign and personal contacts by heads of the various organizations in Sandria and Doville helped to overcome the inertia and the issue was voted. It augured well for favorable action on subsequent requests of the superintendent for an increased budget, rebuilding of the sewer system, and further construction of new buildings. The effect of the volunteers was stated by the superintendent in these words: "Community interest means community pressure for good institutional care."

COMMENTS AND CONCLUSIONS

From the history of the P.S.O. at Doville we can draw certain general conclusions about volunteer programs that are applicable to other places.[1] In essence, our remarks can be divided into three sections: the influence of the program on mental hospital patients, the effect on the volunteers themselves, and the effect on the community.

Today we know that, in general, patients improve in their social relationships if people work intensively with them. Con-

[1] For a comparative interpretation of volunteer activities the reader is referred to: Greenblatt, Milton, Otto von Mering, J. Lawrence Dohan, and David Kantor, "The Use of Volunteers and Other Community Resources" in *The Patient and the Mental Hospital*, edited by Milton Greenblatt and Richard Williams, Free Press, Glencoe, Ill., 1957, chap. 25.

versely, we realize that a patient's illness generally increases in severity with the degree of his isolation from normal human contacts. A patient's personal feeling of isolation is compounded, and the perpetuation of patterns of self-defeat becomes more certain, the longer he remains exclusively confined with his fellow patients. The existence of volunteer services for a hospital, therefore, provides at least a partial solution. Volunteers do not replace the essential services of the basic hospital staff, but their presence can lead to a higher level of total care for a majority of the patients.

It is important to realize that many of the benefits to the patients at Central State Hospital were due to the fact that the volunteers did not try to fulfill all the patients' needs by indiscriminate giving and loving. Rather they tried to set goals that patients in various stages of restoration could handle, and provided the appropriate rewards for this. The close association of ward staff and the volunteers in the planning of activities is a credit to the foresight of both the hospital management and the leaders in the volunteer movement.

Individual volunteers do not remain unaffected by their work. Here is an opportunity for the fulfillment of the basic human needs to give and receive, especially to give without stressing the importance of a measurable return. Few would deny today that this in itself is one of the cardinal principles of mental health.

Some workers must also have experienced a reawakening of social consciousness, of the value to be found in tackling problems on a community basis rather than shifting them to a governmental agency. The progressive industrialization and urbanization of American society, and the simultaneous rise of centralized governmental functions has made it more difficult for the community of individual citizens to accept responsibility for problems. The experience in Sandria and Doville reversed that trend for one community. This has two important results; first, an increased identity with the social welfare of the community as a whole; and second, an improved ability to tackle other community problems. The pride and satisfaction of each volunteer as a citizen cannot be overlooked.

It is but one step from here to the effect on society. Community volunteers can make their towns or cities aware of pressing social problems, and of equal importance can mobilize this concern for pressure on legislative action. The effect on the state legislature in the description we have given is a good case in point.

Perhaps the most important effect on society comes in the changed attitudes toward mental disease. The immediate result is to make the mental patient on visit or after discharge more acceptable in the community. The examples of church attendance and home visits in Doville are pertinent illustrations of this. Although deep-seated fears about mental disease still exist, and will for some time, one of the first breaks in this rigid pattern can come from association with those who are ill and accepting them as a part of the community. Another sign of this effect in the communities around Doville was the increase in the number of visitors to the hospital. In 1954, more than 600 visitors came to the hospital on National Hospital Day, including some from out of state, which is quite different from the six on the occasion that prompted Mrs. Markham to do something about the forgotten people.

We cannot close this account without a final word about the hospital administration. The staff of Central State Hospital demonstrated by their actions two important principles of patient care. First, they operated on the basis that the world of the hospital must be regarded as a transitional social reality for the patients. Second, they devised policies that rested on the belief that a controlled approximation to community living must exist if patients are to be remotivated realistically, and that this can be achieved through the presence of an active volunteer movement.

Most important of all, the volunteer movement showed that change in a positive direction at a state hospital is possible; and that it is primarily a matter of emotional rather than intellectual understanding. The changes that were wrought in the community and at the hospital were not achieved because the means employed were either new or different in themselves. They came about largely as a result of reaffirmation of community social consciousness and of foresightful hospital administration beliefs and practices.

9. Beyond the Legend of Chronicity

THE MAIN THEME which we have tried to present in this book can be summed up in a quotation from an article by Galioni.

> The institutionalized patient is perhaps more a social problem than a psychiatric problem. Therefore, a treatment program should be aimed primarily towards a remotivation of his interest in the environment and a reeducation in his basic techniques of social adjustment.[1]

Up to this point we have presented our main theme in the form of descriptive material, case examples of social remotivation in action. Although there have been some interpretive comments at the end of each case, there has been no systematic endeavor to pull together the varied factors that are involved in remotivation programs. To that task we now turn our efforts. The reader will note as this chapter develops that we have not attempted to put our descriptive material in conceptual or theoretical form. We feel that behavioral theory is not appropriate for this book and have concentrated our efforts on *organizing* the diverse factors in social remotivation of mental patients, and *generalizing* about how change such as we have described can be achieved. Accordingly, our summarization is divided into three sections: first, a consideration of the philosophy which is basic to remotivation; second, pathways, procedures, or techniques in remotivation; and third, a discussion of administrative problems which must be faced if remotivational endeavors are to succeed.

[1] Galioni, E. F., "Intensive Treatment of Back-Ward Patients," VA *Information Bulletin*, Dept. of Medicine and Surgery, Psychiatry and Neurology Service, IB 10-53, February, 1954, p. 43.

THE PHILOSOPHY OF REMOTIVATION

At the outset we owe the reader an explanation for the use of the term "social remotivation," rather than resocialization or rehabilitation. These latter two terms imply a process of making the patient acceptable to others, or fit to live among members of society once again. As such, they do not go far enough, for the intrinsic factor in the change from emotional retreat or withdrawal to social awareness is an emotional commitment to values about life, and the place of the individual in the life scheme. Remotivation of mental patients, as a philosophy, goes deeper than surface techniques, and implies the acceptance by the patient of a set of values which makes him important and worthy as an individual and also as a member of society. The awareness of a value system of this kind and commitment to it by the patient is implied more fully in the term "remotivation" than in resocialization or rehabilitation.

Basic Assumptions

The philosophy of social remotivation has certain basic assumptions which can be stated rather simply. First, the patient must be accepted as a person of value, who has the potentiality for improvement in the future regardless of the degree of observable psychological deterioration. Second, he must be regarded as an individual who through a process of shared interpersonal trust and acceptance on the ward can learn not only to tolerate stress better, but also to use it creatively. Finally, the patient must be given the right not only to have as active a treatment as possible, but also to be alone at times, yet be respected.

The Process of Remotivation—Growth Within Protection

In addition to certain attitudes toward the patient, the philosophy of social remotivation also emphasizes certain attitudes toward the process of treatment. In brief, these are somewhat as follows. In the course of his ward life the patient should experience a mobilization of whatever latent energies he possesses, which should be channeled into a variety of activities that represent graded levels of achievement. These activities should be geared not only to his progressively reawakening resources and skills, but also to the needs of the ward as a community, and to the eventual goal of living again in society outside the hospital. By this process the patient can be led slowly to the rediscovery of himself, and particularly of the inner satisfactions and social rewards that lie in the exercise of choice and of purposeful action.

Goals—Replacing the Principle of Least Effort

As was implied in the basic assumptions, one of the goals in social remotivation is a changed staff-patient relationship. The anticipated relationship can be described in a number of ways. For example, one might say that the goal is a transfer of the efforts of ward personnel from a primary concern with control measures and ward housekeeping duties to a concern with the job of helping patients. Essentially this goal seeks a release of energy, freeing the power which is tied up in carrying out the ward routine, so that it may be invested in the lives and problems of the patients. Once this transfer of energy has taken place, the ward routine can be utilized for therapeutic purposes, the "musts" of the daily schedule can be changed from monotonous drudgery to a valuable learning experience.

One might look at the goal of a changed staff-patient relationship in another way, that of the change from a contractual relationship to a personal one. In the former case the obligations of the nurse or aide toward the patient are thought of mainly in terms of relationships such as those which might be stated in a union contract, of carrying out certain procedures of care and control toward the patient which are largely invariant regardless of the particular personalities of given patients. Patients come and go but the obligations of the job remain the same. In a personal relationship the needs and feelings of particular patients dominate the obligations of staff members within, of course, the realities of an administrative framework. As patients come and go the demands of the job change. To use a colloquial expression, the personal relationship can be thought of as operating "above and beyond the call of duty," if duty is thought of as the job description in the civil service personnel book.

Another set of goals pertains to the future of individual patients. It is the hope that all patients might eventually be discharged to the community, but for some patients this may be expecting the development of a level of competence of which they are not capable. In this case the *principle of limited goals* comes into operation. Although a particular patient may not be able to handle the stress of living outside the hospital, he can be brought to the level of a better adjustment within the hospital community. In the description of the Habit Training Ward or "Cafeteria Training" there were many patients who could be helped from the stage of severe psychological and physiological regression to a stage where they could become useful members of hospital society, taking a share of social responsibility and establishing meaningful contacts with other patients and the staff. For these patients the concept of a limited goal was important.

One could describe the principle of limited goals in terms of a dual discharge system, discharge of the patient to the community, or discharge to a better ward within the hospital. Acceptance of this philosophy dignifies the work of the staff and provides a potent source of motivation for patients to give up inappropriate, self-defeating behavior.

By way of summary, the philosophy of remotivation is the antithesis of the Legend of Chronicity. It cannot accept the interpretation of chronic that means an inability to improve, that bespeaks a hopelessness for any and all therapeutic efforts, that releases the staff from a feeling of personal obligation to lead their charges back to sanity. Furthermore, the philosophy of remotivation is not to be confused with one that emphasizes space and person manipulation. Techniques that move patients around are of little value unless the patient has a sense of personal participation and choice. They are also of little value without a personal investment in their success by those who administer them, plus an abiding belief that the patient can improve.

PATHWAYS IN REMOTIVATION

One of the essential ingredients for a successful remotivation program is the training and utilization of meaningful people for patients. The importance of this is clear in the philosophy that underlies remotivation and it has been demonstrated in each of the case histories that have been presented in this book. No more important factor could be chosen to begin a discussion of pathways in remotivation.

Aides and Others

Any remotivation program over the long run or with large numbers of patients will not succeed without the training of good aides. Those on the hospital staff who have the closest and most continuing contact with patients are the aides. Therefore, potentially they are the greatest source of help, or hindrance, in the slow process of helping the psychotic patient reestablish confidence in himself and in other human beings. The emphasis on the strategic importance of aides has implications in two directions, for those whose responsibility it is to administer treatment wards, and for those whose responsibility it is to manage the total hospital policy and program. The implications for the latter group will come under discussion later in this chapter; our present interest concerns the physician and nurse who have responsibility for patients on a ward.

If we were to list specific principles or techniques of remotivation, the first would be that *aides must be made part of the treatment team and share in the responsibility for patient care and improvement.* This can be accomplished in a number of ways. At the very least the aides should be included in regular meetings with other members of the ward staff where there is not only opportunity to discuss individual cases in the light of treatment plans, but where each aide can feel free to bring out feelings, attitudes, and ideas about the patients. The important factor is the acceptance of the aide's observations and ideas, and the integration of them, perhaps after reworking in the staff conference, into treatment plans. The inclusion of the aide in ward meetings not only imparts a sense of responsibility but also provides an opportunity for the physician or nurse to help the aide come to more mature and progressive ideas about work with patients.

Another way that aides can be given a greater share in responsibility for patients is seen in the Ward Mothers program, which was described in Chapter 6. Here the aide had the opportunity to form close relationships with a small number of patients and was encouraged to help the patient utilize this relationship as a testing ground for improved relationships with other patients on the ward or people in other parts of the hospital.

It will not be possible to establish programs comparable to the Ward Mothers on many wards, for patients of a relatively good level of psychological integration are necessary and the number of staff required may be prohibitive. Nevertheless, it is a proto-type of the highest utilization of the energy and abilities of aides and should not be pushed out of mind, even on regressed wards.

Closely associated with increased responsibility for aides is a new conception of the place that occupational therapists, physical therapists, recreational therapists, and other ancillary personnel can take in the ward situation. Too often there is rivalry between the ward staff and the ancillary services. For example, members of the occupational therapy department may feel that only they, as professionals, are capable of working with patients in arts and crafts and other activities associated with occupational therapy. Furthermore, these activities too often take place in special sec-tions of the hospital, making it difficult for many patients to participate.

The second principle or technique of remotivation can then be stated as broadening the role of members of the ancillary services to make them consultants to individual ward programs, resource persons who possess special skills and information that can contribute to a more effective treat-ment program. This has two advantages, raising the status of those in the ancillary services, and giving them a share in the responsi-bility for patient improvement in a much broader sense than they usually possess.

In each of the case studies presented in this book there was an effective utilization of O.T., R.T., P.T., as they are called, but perhaps the clearest illustration was in the description of "cafe-teria training." The reader will remember that as soon as some success was achieved in habit training, activities were organized around the long tables. At first these were simple (burlap bags were taken apart and step by step made into soft balls), but gradually the activities became more complex (cloth was cut up for stuffing and toy animals were made). The skills of the occupational therapy department were essential in planning these activities, in securing the materials, and in helping to move on to more complex tasks. Members of the ward staff could handle the regular supervision of the patients around the long tables, but depended a great deal on the consulting activities of the regular members of the occupational therapy department.

One of the keys to successful remotivation is the bringing of meaningful circuits of activity within the social setting of the ward, where ward staff can work in these circuits as important persons for the patients. To this end the members of the ancillary services can play a most important role in planning and design, as well as ongoing consultation and evaluation.

Breaking the Distance Barrier

One of the problems on a psychiatric ward is the emotional distance between staff and patients. In the traditional Museum Ward atmosphere the distance between staff and patients is great, and it is not easy to break the emotional barrier that separates them. Yet it is crucial to remotivation that members of the ward staff become meaningful people in a positive sense in the lives of patients. *The third principle or technique of remotivation, therefore, is that all the ward staff should be used to break staff-patient distance, by having the staff participate in the patient society, by having them portray socially acceptable and "normal" standards of behavior on the ward.* To accomplish this end patients must also be brought into the sphere of responsibility for their actions and must plan with staff for ward life. For example, formal and informal meetings of patients and personnel need to be held to increase the feeling of ingroup identification, or group solidarity. The difference between what is a "staff person" and what is a "patient person" can thereby be diminished or deemphasized. The important by-product will often be a consensual validation of standards of conduct, meaning that energy spent on control measures can be shifted to energy spent on patient work.

The interaction of staff and patients can be implemented through joint efforts toward changes in the physical arrangements of the ward, or plans for redecoration. Even on the habit training ward the clothesroom man was given responsibility for planning with ward staff about painting his room and making it more attractive in other ways. On other wards the patients worked with aides in making draperies for the ward and shared responsibility for seeing that they were hung properly. In the description of the industrial ward it was noted that staff and patients shared in the planning of parties and also in the fun of the party itself. Therefore, staff-patient interaction can come about not only in improving the ward but in the enjoyment of each other's company through recreation.

In all ward situations there is a direct, though inverse, relationship between staff distance from the patients and a sense of social identity. As the distance decreases through staff-patient interaction there is a corresponding increase in feelings of interpersonal trust and a renewed sense of social identity.

Utilization of Patient Society

As Caudill[1] has pointed out, patients are not isolated individuals, but are members of a social structure in which, even in a rudimentary form, there are shared beliefs and values which are translated into action through a system of social roles and cliques. Patients are aware of what is going on around them, and their behavior is related to the situation in which they find themselves. If one accepts this assumption of a dynamic relationship between patient and environment, then the fourth principle of remotivation can be stated as follows: *a change in one aspect of the patient's social life is followed by changes within himself and in other aspects of his social life.*

Once a change is introduced in one aspect of a social situation the perception of individuals in the situation is changed and changed perception usually leads to new and different behavior. This can be illustrated by activities on the lobotomy ward. The

[1] Caudill, William, and Edward Stainbrook, "Some Covert Effects of Communication Difficulties in a Psychiatric Hospital," *Psychiatry*, vol. 17, 1954, pp. 27–40.

first change was the introduction of cosmetics, which altered per-
ceptions sufficiently so that it was felt necessary to obtain brightly
colored head scarfs, then attractive dresses. Patients were very
much aware of these changes and reflected them in improved
social behavior, less soiling, and increased social interaction with
other patients and staff.

Acceptance of the fact that patients are members of a social
structure has another important implication, directly related to
the therapeutic process. The primary group of the moment to
which a person belongs has much meaning to him, whether this
meaning be of a positive or negative nature. If the meaning is in a
positive, supportive direction there is always the potentiality
within the group process for the binding up of emotional wounds
and the strengthening of the individual against future stress.
Therefore, we can state the fifth principle of remotivation by saying that *remotivational programs should utilize the idea that the sick can
help the sicker and that within patient groups themselves there are potential
sources of help toward more mature social interaction.*

We illustrated this principle at some length in the description
of the Family of Elders, showing how regressed and incontinent
patients could often be helped toward improvement by the interest and support of other patients. This was true not only for
incontinent patients but also for those who were cantankerous or
resistive to the efforts of ward personnel in trying to bring them
into ward activities. The reader will remember that the charge
aide for the Family of Elders fostered these helping relationships
among patients whenever she saw common interests arising or
the growing concern of one patient for another relative to aspects
of the ward routine. A clinical director of one of the hospitals
visited by the observer remarked to him that there were sound
learning possibilities in the "sick help the sicker" pattern.
Patients can be helped to a more realistic awareness of their
own problems when they realize that others are more disturbed,
or regressed, or unhappy than they are, that someone else has
a cross harder to bear. This is a form of teaching by contrast,
a technique long used by educators, and by psychotherapists.
In addition, the mobilization of energies toward helping another

individual is valuable in that it activates an outgo of emotional effort, and thus starts a reversal of the narcissistic overconcern which is so characteristic of the mental patient.

Turning more toward the individual patient, it is important to remember that patients differ in terms of their experience and their problems. Although this statement may appear only to accentuate the obvious, it has implications for patient improvement. The observer noted the recurring fact in hospital after hospital that patients got better doing many different things. The next principle can then be stated: *specific media in remotivation are not so important as the purpose behind the techniques and the interpersonal closeness of staff and patients in shared activities.*

We do not mean that one can ignore specific techniques, for the assignment of ward responsibilities must be dovetailed with the patient's past performance and the significance of the role he plays in the social structure of the ward. Our main emphasis here is that one approach will work for one patient that will not work for another; therefore, one cannot rely on techniques alone. Success will depend on finding an activity for the patient that is meaningful in the light of his position in the social structure, and on implementing such an activity through close interpersonal support by ward personnel and other patients.

A final point needs to be made in considering the implications of patient social structure. Mental patients have withdrawn from the vicissitudes of life in normal society; hence, their social structure is directed toward an equilibrium that shuts out contact with and thoughts about life on the outside. The process of social remotivation attempts to change the focus of patient social structure by orienting it toward social relations as they exist outside the hospital and toward an equilibrium that seeks contact with society on the outside. To sum this up in the seventh principle of remotivation: *every attempt should be made to introduce activities on the ward that are as normal as possible and oriented toward future life outside the hospital.*

Insistence on the necessity of close relationships between staff and patients is in support of this principle but it also implies a changed attitude toward relatives and other people from the community. Too often relatives are regarded as people for the social workers to handle. If the ward staff are oriented toward control and maintenance, as on the Museum Ward, relatives can be disruptive influences, for they stir up patients and throw the ward routine out of balance. In contrast, the process of social remotivation utilizes relatives, and others, as resources for treatment by providing a continuous background of normal social relationships against which the patient can better see his own distorted relationships. In each of the ward situations that have been described in this book relatives have been used as resource persons for treatment. In some cases they helped to plan parties or other forms of entertainment. In other cases they worked with patients on planning changes in the physical environment of the ward, and helped the patients do the work, or they brought in furniture, clothes, food, and other things that helped make the ward seem less like an isolated society and more like an extension of the normal community. The volunteer movement is a direct application of the same principle and the extensive description we gave of one volunteer organization should not make it necessary to repeat examples at this juncture. We should reiterate one point, however, that the therapeutic use of relatives and volunteers not only helps patients but is important to the long-range goal of changing public attitudes toward the mentally ill. In other words, use of relatives and volunteers has therapeutic value for the community as well as for the patients, and in the long run changed attitudes in the community may be one of the most important factors in facilitating the care of people who have mental illness.

Planning—Over and Under

When the ward staff begin to think about the problems of individual patients and the ways in which they can facilitate changes in patient behavior they have automatically gone into the stage of planning. There are dangers and fears inherent in planning, however, which need some discussion and clarification, for it is easy to overplan (and lose the patient in the process) or to concentrate too much on interpersonal relationships and not be ready for the patient when he reaches a new growth plateau.

Overplanning results from the phobia that you cannot leave anything to chance and as such can represent a defense against insecurity in interpersonal relationships on the part of the staff. To a certain extent the master plan and continuous process on the Moving Ward illustrate the dangers of overplanning and the ease with which planning can become a defense. On the Moving Ward there is little time for close staff-patient involvement, thanks to the master schedule.

The process of social remotivation requires an alertness to situations as they arise, a flexibility of approach that allows changes in activities, an imagination that welcomes new ideas and new relationships. Furthermore, we suggest that there is value in realization by patients that the staff are not always completely secure or omnipotent, or all knowing. Part of the process of growing up, whether from childhood to adulthood, or from patient to nonpatient, lies in the awareness that others do not always have the answers and that one must sometimes look within oneself for a decision about the right direction to take. Realization by both staff and patients that the physician or nurse or aide does not always know the answer can contribute toward growth in becoming a regular member of society.

Danger at the other end of the planning process occurs when there is not a ready reception for the patient at his new level of adjustment. One could characterize underplanning in this sense as a stalemate at plateaus, whereas social remotivation emphasizes the existence of a gradient within the ward complex and within a set of wards. Activities on the habit training ward provide an illustration of gradient, the first plateau being toilet training, the next being ward worker, and finally that of patient helper and supervisor. The chapter on "cafeteria training" showed how the gradient can be extended beyond the complex of a specific ward by transferring or discharging a patient from wards B-1 and B-2 to Ward C-7, and eventually to the D building, the process shown in the figure on page 153. We might summarize these ideas by stating another principle of remotivation. *Flexibility and imagination, plus a willingness to admit that staff are not omnipotent, are essential to remotivation and counteract overplan-*

ning. At the same time utilization of a gradient of adjustment and social roles within and between wards prevents stagnation at plateaus of achievement and counteracts underplanning.

The topic of planning cannot be left without one final comment. Almost any treatment plan that is new soon becomes old, a maxim that is so obvious that it easily becomes forgotten. Thus, an essential ingredient in the planning process is a periodic reassessment of changes brought about in new treatment processes. Regular evaluation of progress was essential to the success of the volunteer program which we described in Chapter 8 and was one of the important factors in preventing stagnation at plateaus of achievement.

Remotivation as an Experience for Staff

Realizing the ever present danger of boring the reader with repetition or causing him to think that we are reflecting on his intelligence, we would like to discuss some of the potential effects of remotivation programs on those who care for patients. Much of what we will now say has already been implied; yet its importance for both administration and patient care cannot be overemphasized.

On a ward where a program of social remotivation is in operation the nurses and aides can learn to live with patients in terms of ward reality and not just in terms of a superimposed set of controls. Through the utilization of meaningful and purposeful ward activities personnel have the opportunity to learn something about the art of casual conversation, that is, to listen to patient complaints, tolerate and be comfortable with silences, and practice different tactical approaches to difficult patients. Furthermore, awareness of ward reality means that a direct and immediate access to patients is present and it is more difficult for patients to become lost or forgotten and left to their own devices.

Staff on a remotivation ward have a different status in the eyes of patients. They are not regarded merely as personnel paid to give service, mete out punishment and kindness, but rather as interested representatives from the outside world who have a stake in the emotional life of the patient. Under these conditions ward personnel by and large rise above themselves in their ability to care for patients.

When staff are immersed in ward activities and learn to share in long-range disposition and discharge planning, they develop better patterns of observation of patient skills and interests, of work habits and performance patterns. They become more aware of how the ward environment can prepare the patient for discharge to a different ward or to the community outside. In short, they come to see patient care as a process of growth instead of a state of custody.

Participation in a program of remotivation means that ward personnel are more effective in making interpretations to relatives and others from the community about mental illness and the effects of institutionalization. They can show relatives how the shift from the hospital to the community on the outside is a continuous process rather than a disconnected one and can help the relatives contribute to patient adjustment at home. In turn this enhances the status of ward personnel in their own eyes, for they feel a part of the whole process, not just a fragment of it.

Finally, through the process of remotivation ward staff and members of the ancillary services come to realize that they have special competences which others in the hospital can use profitably. Thus, aides can overcome their traditional fears of sharing responsibility with occupational therapists, and the status of the latter can be raised as he or she becomes a consultant or specialized resource person. Rapport and cooperation between ward staff and other hospital personnel can be heightened, to the mutual benefit of staff as well as patients.

ADMINISTRATION AND REMOTIVATION

At the beginning of the Introduction, we noted many of the frustrating problems that are of everyday concern to those who are responsible for the administration of large state mental hospitals. The shortage of personnel, inadequate and crowded buildings, and small budgets are realities that administrators cannot avoid. Changes and improvements become luxuries that must be considered and weighed carefully before they can be purchased.

The description of the process of social remotivation which has been presented in the case histories and in the previous section of this chapter easily fits the idea of a luxury and may raise questions in the minds of many on the administrative staff. Is it feasible to support active remotivation programs in large state hospitals? Will the cost disrupt the budgeting of money and personnel and disturb the precarious balance that now exists? These questions have to be answered by those who make the administrative decisions in individual hospitals; we can only discuss certain issues that are relevant to the problem.

At the outset, it must be admitted that any long-term success with remotivation programs requires both the philosophical and material support of the hospital administration. In many hospitals, attempts at remotivation are "grass roots" affairs at first, starting on one or two wards where some of the aides, or a physician or nurse, feel that something can and needs to be done to turn patients toward more mature social relations. In some cases there may be tacit approval from the medical and administrative staff, but it is in the form of a "wait and see" attitude that puts pressure on those running the program to succeed or else lose the possibility of trying again. In tacit approval of this sort there is the idea that enough rope will be given for the remotivation people to fashion a worthwhile program or "hang themselves." If, indeed, the remotivation program in a particular hospital is a "grass roots" affair, it may bring about some anxious moments for the administration. Not having thought it feasible to do something to change patterns of patient care, the administration may ask themselves why they did not think of the idea, or may feel that if it does not work out they will be in an embarrassing position as far as the public or other hospitals are concerned. Furthermore, if apparent success is in sight for the remotivation program it may bring about an agonizing reappraisal of the whole pattern of patient care in the hospital.

The first stage of success of a remotivation program is crucial, for if it does not have the philosophical and material support of the administration at that point it may wither away from "administrative malnutrition." The importance of firm and continued backing by those in the hospital responsible for policy and the allocation of goods and personnel cannot be overstressed.

Stating the importance of administrative support does not avoid consideration of problems that administration must face. Perhaps the most pressing of these will be related to personnel. Initiation of remotivation programs requires the judicious redistribution of personnel. It may appear at first that it also requires the addition of sizable numbers of new aides and nurses. Indeed, in the programs that have been described in the preceding chapters a concentration of ward personnel was required to establish the habit training ward or the procedures on the House of Miracles ward. However, once a remotivation ward had been in operation for some time two things happened. In the first place, the energies of staff were less tied up in the requirements of control and housekeeping and increasingly freed for work with patients. One nurse put it this way: "When I don't have to be busy just keeping the lid on the ward or keeping it clean, I know what I can do." Personnel thereby become more efficient in terms of the utilization of their ability for therapy. In the second place, patients come to take more responsibility for maintenance and household tasks as part of the therapeutic process. Not only is this a positive part of their improvement but it relieves hospital staff of some of their duties. To sum up, the initiation of remotivation programs requires a concentration of hospital personnel in certain areas, but once the programs are well established a redistribution of personnel can take place and they can be employed more efficiently.

An important aspect of the personnel problem lies in the utilization of aides. We have noted that the process of remotivation gives higher status to the aide and makes him an important part of the therapeutic program. Retraining of aides is therefore an important step that can be undertaken by the administration. Any hospital can institute aide classes in which aides can be taught to understand better the reasons behind patient behavior and the implications of different kinds of staff-patient interaction. The reader will remember that Mrs. Cosgrove, the charge aide on the habit training ward, was a member of the first aide class at

Lynwood State Hospital, and that she attributed much of her success with her patients to the learning experience in aide classes. Inservice education for aides can improve their ability to work with patients, can make them more useful, and can be an important first step in raising their status. Furthermore, once a remotivation program is under way, the participating wards can be the training ground or the laboratory for the aides in training. Training and utilization of aides in remotivation becomes an expanding process, the more that are trained the more energy there is released from control and maintenance functions for patient help.

Increase in the number of personnel and improved physical facilities by themselves will not produce proportionately greater or more lasting results. Furthermore, this is unrealistic for many of our large state hospitals. Instead, existing resources need to be reexamined, existing patterns of care reappraised, and present facilities more effectively utilized. Some of these things will not be easy or convenient from the administrative point of view, but as patterns of expedience are broken and a positive philosophy of remotivation adopted there will be solid gain.

EPILOGUE

Lest we lead the reader into believing that the process of social remotivation as it has been described in this book answers all the problems of care and treatment of mental patients it should be emphasized that *the* basis for therapeutic efficacy does not exist. The social self-renewal and remotivation of a patient is a slow learning process that is based on six rehabilitative ingredients, some of which have been discussed at length, others only fleetingly in this book.

The first of the rehabilitative ingredients is *verbal therapy*, exemplified in the term, "the word doctor," and having its clearest exposition in close interpersonal psychotherapy. Verbal therapy occurs on the ward also, in relations between the nurse, aide, and patient. It occurs when the aide and nurse learn to be good listeners, when they can tolerate silences by the patient, when they can help the patient reestablish channels of communication with others through casual conversation. The good "word doctor" is one like Mrs. Cosgrove, or Mrs. Harlan, and many others, whose words with the patient are appropriate to the ongoing situation, to his needs at the moment, and arouse within him the need to change.

Next comes *somatic therapy*, exemplified in the term, "the touch doctor." Somatic therapy is a most important part of the treatment of the mental patient, for electric convulsive therapy or insulin coma can frequently hasten the shift from withdrawal and regression to contact with others. The tranquilizing drugs are useful in controlling agitation and free anxiety, thus making the patient more amenable to the efforts of staff to establish more mature reactions to stress and improved social interaction. We have not discussed somatic therapy further in this book because its beneficial effects are well known, yet it must be made clear that often it is essential for the improvement or recovery of the mental patient.

Third, there is *work therapy*, characterized by "the work doctor." We have shown that occupational therapy and industrial placement within the hospital can contribute a great deal to the healing of the mental patient, to the extent that the work has meaning for the patient and is not just drudgery. The phrase "meaningful circuits of activity within the ward setting" illustrated this third rehabilitative ingredient for the disturbed or regressed patient. For others, the activity was related to an environment beyond the ward, and eventually to life outside the hospital.

Then comes *play therapy*, seen in the term, "the play doctor." Recreation is part of mature social life and is essential to healing. The recreational therapist, as a consultant to ward programs, or as director of activities off the ward, plays a key role in remotivation. The example of the Hawaiian party, described in connection with the industrial ward (Chapter 6, Ward Mothers) showed how recreation could eventually be taken over largely by patients. Activities of the volunteers working with the recreational therapist on closed wards showed how it could be integrated into the ward complex. When a withdrawn schizophrenic patient, whom no one had been able to reach, responds to a musical concert by tapping his feet and swaying in time to the music, one sees how play therapy as a rehabilitative ingredient is important for therapeutic efficacy.

Another rehabilitative ingredient is *food therapy*, exemplified in the phrase, "the food doctor." Eating is often a symbolic experience, indicative of emotional closeness and the family board, hallowed by sacrament and dignified by tradition and social gathering. In the Family Room experience the use of food went beyond the mere satisfaction of essential physical need to the gratification of everyday emotional needs for sharing and belonging. Too often a neglected aspect of patient care, the preparation and serving of food, can no longer be omitted from therapeutic planning for the mental patient.

Finally, there is *spirit therapy*, faith in individuals plus grace, shown in "the spirit doctor." Religion has always been an integral part of man's life, a way of answering the perplexing questions of existence, of pain and suffering, of death, and of the place of the individual in the design of things. Mental disease does not mean that these questions disappear; indeed, they are frequently intensified, and hospitals are coming more and more to realize the contribution of the priest, minister, and rabbi to the process of groping back to sanity. In the chapter on volunteers we showed that one way in which the community can be brought to the lives of patients is through religious services and hymn sings on the wards, patient choirs, and the participation of patients in worship services off the hospital grounds.

The six basic rehabilitative ingredients can be effective only insofar as they exist in a system of action that goes beyond the Legend of Chronicity. The undergirding common feature to their effective use is the philosophy of social remotivation as we have outlined it in these pages. In the spirit of that philosophy the individual patient is regarded as a person of worth and promise and the staff seek to develop in their patients controls from within to replace those which they at times have found necessary to impose from without. Finally, in the spirit of that philosophy, the staff seek to replace authoritarian (proceeding from status and tradition) approaches with the utilization of authoritative (proceeding from knowledge and understanding) patterns of patient care.

Selected Bibliography

Selected Bibliography

Dealing with Philosophy and Technique
of Intensive Environmental Treatment of
Mental Patients

ABRAHAMS, JOSEPH, "Preliminary Report of an Experience in the Group Psychotherapy of Schizophrenics," *American Journal of Psychiatry*, vol. 104, April, 1948, pp. 613–617.

ADLAND, M. L., "Personnel—Effect on Patients," *Neuropsychiatry*, vol. 3, 1955, pp. 110–131.

APPEL, K. E., and A. E. SCHEFLEN, "Current Concepts of Psychiatry in Relation to Hospital Treatment," *Neuropsychiatry*, vol. 3, 1955, p. 88–109.

AZIMA, H. S., and E. D. WITTKOWER, "Gratification of Basic Needs in Treatment of Schizophrenics," *Psychiatry*, vol. 19, May, 1956, pp. 121–129.

BAKER, A. A., and J. G. THORPE, "Deteriorated Psychotic Patients: Their Treatment and Its Assessment," *Journal of Mental Science*, vol. 102, October, 1956, pp. 780–789.

BAKER, A. A., and J. G. THORPE, "Some Simple Measures of Schizophrenic Deterioration," *Journal of Mental Science*, vol. 102, October, 1956, pp. 838–846.

BAKER, H. B., "The Psychology of Clothing as a Treatment Aid," *Mental Hygiene*, vol. 39, January, 1955, pp. 94–98.

BARNARD, R. I., L. L. ROBBINS, and F. M. TETZLAFF, "The Day Hospital as an Extension of Psychiatric Treatment," *Bulletin of Menninger Clinic*, vol. 16, March, 1952, pp. 50–56.

BARTEMEIER, L. H., "Therapeutic Results in Mental Hospitals with a Minimum of Professional Personnel," *American Journal of Psychiatry*, vol. 113, December, 1956, pp. 515–518.

BATEMAN, J. F., and H. W. DUNHAM, "The State Mental Hospital as a Specialized Community Experience," *American Journal of Psychiatry*, vol. 105, December, 1948, pp. 445–448.

BELL, G. M., "A Mental Hospital with Open Doors," *International Journal of Social Psychiatry*, vol. 1, January, 1955, pp. 42–48.

BENNETT, D. H., and J. P. S. ROBERTSON, "The Effects of Habit Training on Chronic Schizophrenic Patients," *Journal of Mental Science*, vol. 101, July, 1955, pp. 664–672.

BETTELHEIM, BRUNO, "Mental Health and Current Mores," *American Journal of Orthopsychiatry*, vol. 22, January, 1952, pp. 76–88.

BETTELHEIM, BRUNO, and EMMY SYLVESTER, "A Therapeutic Milieu," *American Journal of Orthopsychiatry*, vol. 18, April, 1948, pp. 191–206.

BIERER, JOSHUA, and F. P. HALDANE, "A Self-Governed Patients' Social Club in a Public Mental Hospital," *Journal of Mental Science*, vol. 87, July, 1941, pp. 419–424.

BIKALES, V. W., "Drama Therapy at Winter Veterans Administration Hospital," *Bulletin of Menninger Clinic*, vol. 13, 1949, pp. 127–133.

BLAIR, DONALD A. S., "The Therapeutic Social Club: An Important Measure of Social Rehabilitation in the Treatment of Psychiatric Cases," *Mental Hygiene*, vol. 39, January, 1955, pp. 54–62.

BLASSINGILLE, B., "Rehabilitation of Negro Post-Leukotomy Patients," *Journal of Nervous and Mental Disease*, vol. 121, June, 1955, pp. 527–534.

BOBIS, B. R., R. M. HARRISON, and L. TRAUB, "Activity Group Therapy," *American Journal of Occupational Therapy*, vol. 9, no. 1, 1955, pp. 19–21.

BOND, E. D., "Therapeutic Forces in Early American Hospitals," *American Journal of Psychiatry*, vol. 113, November, 1956, pp. 407–408.

BULLARD, D. M., "The Organization of Psychoanalytic Procedure in the Hospital," *Journal of Nervous and Mental Disease*, vol. 91, June, 1940, pp. 697–703.

CAMERON, J. L., R. D. LAING, and A. McGHIE, "Patient and Nurse: Effects of Environmental Changes in the Care of Chronic Schizophrenics," *Lancet*, vol. 28, December, 1955, pp. 1384–1386.

CASE, M. E., "The Forgotten Ones: An Exploratory Project in the Use of Group Activities for the Treatment of Deteriorated Psychotic Patients," *Smith College Studies in Social Work*, vol. 21, 1951, pp. 199–231.

Cosin, L. Z., "The Place of the Day Hospital in the Geriatric Unit," *International Journal of Social Psychiatry*, vol. 1, February, 1955, pp. 33–41.

Cowen, J. R., "Administrative Economy on a State Hospital Ward," *Psychiatric Quarterly*, vol. 29, no. 4, 1955, pp. 612–620.

Croog, S. H., "Patient Government: Some Aspects of Participation and Social Background on Two Psychiatric Wards," *Psychiatry*, vol. 19, May, 1956, pp. 203–207.

Cumming, Elaine, I. L. W. Clancey, and John Cumming, "Improving Patient Care Through Organizational Changes in the Mental Hospital," *Psychiatry*, vol. 19, August, 1956, pp. 249–261.

Cumming, Elaine, and John Cumming, "The Locus of Power in a Large Mental Hospital," *Psychiatry*, vol. 19, November, 1956, pp. 361–369.

Currier, M. E., M. Helmle, and M. Caron, "Geriatric Habit Training," *Psychiatric Quarterly* SUPPLEMENT, vol. 29, 1955, pp. 38–42.

DuBois, F. S., "Rehabilitation and Occupational Therapy," *American Journal of Psychiatry*, vol. 113, January, 1957, pp. 637–641.

Enelow, A. J., "The Environmental Treatment of Psychosis," *Psychiatric Quarterly* SUPPLEMENT, vol. 26, 1952, pp. 44–52.

Ewalt, J. R., "Mental Health Problems Affecting Social Relations," *Annals of the American Academy of Political and Social Sciences*, vol. 286, March, 1953, pp. 74–80.

Feifel, H. S., and A. D. Schwartz, "Group Psychotherapy with Acutely Disturbed Psychotic Patients," *Journal of Consulting Psychology*, vol. 17, 1953, pp. 113–121.

Field, S. P., R. J. Lucero, and A. Rechtschaffen, "Cross-Validation and Follow-up of a State Hospital 'Total Push' Program for Regressed Schizophrenics," *Journal of Clinical Psychology*, vol. 9, 1953, pp. 394–395.

Forrer, G. R., "Work Therapy Program at Northville State Hospital (Michigan)," *American Journal of Occupational Therapy*, vol. 9, no. 4, 1955, pp. 154–155.

Fromm-Reichmann, Frieda, "Problems of Therapeutic Management in a Psychoanalytic Hospital," *Psychoanalytic Quarterly*, vol. 16, no. 3, 1947, pp. 325–356.

Galioni, E. F., F. H. Adams, and F. F. Tallman, "Intensive Treatment of Back-Ward Patients: A Controlled Pilot Study," *American Journal of Psychiatry*, vol. 109, February, 1953, pp. 576–583.

GARDNER, J., and N. C. MORGAN, "Industrial Therapy," *American Journal of Occupational Therapy*, vol. 7, no. 6, 1953, pp. 1–6.

GINZBERG, RAPHAEL, "Geriatric Ward Psychiatry," *American Journal of Psychiatry*, vol. 110, October, 1953, pp. 296–300.

GOLDFARB, A. I., and JACK SHEPS, "Psychotherapy of the Aged: III Brief Therapy of Interrelated Psychological and Somatic Disorders," *Psychosomatic Medicine*, vol. 16, May–June, 1954, pp. 209–219.

GREENBLATT, MILTON, RICHARD H. YORK, and ESTHER LUCILE BROWN, *From Custodial to Therapeutic Patient Care in Mental Hospitals*. Russell Sage Foundation, New York, 1955.

HAUN, PAUL, "Are You a Hostess to Your Patient-Guests? Opportunities for Dietitians in Mental Hospitals," *Journal of the American Dietetic Association*, vol. 30, November, 1954, pp. 1140–1146.

HYDE, R. W., and H. C. SOLOMON, "Patient Government: A New Form of Group Therapy," *Digest of Neurology and Psychology*, vol. 18, 1950, pp. 207–218.

JONES, MAXWELL, *The Therapeutic Community: A New Treatment Method in Psychiatry*. Basic Books, New York, 1953.

JONES, M. I., and R. A. MATTHEWS, "The Application of the Therapeutic Community Principle to a State Mental Health Programme," *British Journal of Medical Psychology*, vol. 29, 1956, pp. 57–62.

KAMMAN, G. R., and others, "Critical Evaluation of a Total Push Program for Regressed Schizophrenics in a State Hospital," *Psychiatric Quarterly*, vol. 28, October, 1954, pp. 650–667.

KRAUS, P. S., "Considerations and Problems of Ward Care for Schizophrenic Patients: Formulation of a Total Responsibility Program," *Psychiatry*, vol. 17, August, 1954, pp. 283–292.

LAY, MADELEINE, "Helping the Patients Deal with Anxiety-Producing Factors in His Reality Situation," *Neuropsychiatry*, vol. 3, 1955, pp. 132–152.

LINDEN, MAURICE E., "Silent Partner in Mental Health," *Mental Hygiene*, vol. 40, January, 1956, pp. 90–95.

MARTIN, D. V., M. M. GLATT, and K. F. WEEKS, "An Experimental Unit for the Community Treatment of Neurosis," *Journal of Mental Science*, vol. 100, October, 1954, pp. 983–989.

MARTIN, M. G., "A Practical Treatment Program for a Mental Hospital 'Back' Ward," *American Journal of Psychiatry*, vol. 106, April, 1950, pp. 758–760.

McCULLOUGH, W. E., "Report of an Integrated Therapeutic Program: A Three-Year Ward Experiment," *Psychiatric Quarterly*, vol. 29, April, 1955, pp. 280–309.

McMILLEN, LOUISE, "Occupational Therapy: A Definitely Prescribed Treatment for the Neuropsychiatric Patient," *American Journal of Occupational Therapy*, vol. 3, no. 1, 1949, pp. 3–9.

MEISLIN, JACK, "The Psychiatric Sheltered Workshop in Rehabilitation of the Mentally Ill," *Archives of Physical Medicine and Rehabilitation*, vol. 35, April, 1954, pp. 224–227.

MENNINGER, W. C., "The Functions of the Psychiatric Hospital," *Bulletin of Menninger Clinic*, vol. 6, July, 1942, pp. 109–116.

MENNINGER, W. C., "Psychiatric Hospital Therapy Designed to Meet Unconscious Needs," *American Journal of Psychiatry*, vol. 93, September, 1936, pp. 347–360.

MERRY, J., "An Experiment in a Chronic Psychotic Ward," *British Journal of Medical Psychology*, vol. 29, 1956, pp. 287–293.

MEYERSON, ABRAHAM, "Theory and Principles of the 'Total Push' Method in the Treatment of Chronic Schizophrenia," *American Journal of Psychiatry*, vol. 95, March, 1939, pp. 1197–1204.

MILLER, D. H., "The Rehabilitation of Chronic Open-Ward Neuropsychiatric Patients," *Psychiatry*, vol. 17, November, 1954, pp. 347–358.

MILLER, D. H., and JOHN CLANCY, "An Approach to the Social Rehabilitation of Chronic Psychotic Patients," *Psychiatry*, vol. 15, November, 1952, pp. 435–443.

MODLIN, H. C., and M. FARIS, "Follow-up Study of Psychiatric Team Functioning," *Bulletin of Menninger Clinic*, vol. 18, November, 1954, pp. 242–251.

NICOLAOU, G. T., "Evaluation of Ward Occupational Therapy with Regressed Patients," *Psychiatric Quarterly* SUPPLEMENT, vol. 25, 1951, pp. 202–205.

O'REILLY, P. O., and J. R. HANDFORTH, "Occupational Therapy with 'Refractory' Patients," *American Journal of Psychiatry*, vol. 111, April, 1955, pp. 763–766.

OWENS, L., and G. S. WHITE, "Observations on Food Acceptance during Mental Illness," *Journal of the American Dietetic Association*, vol. 30, November, 1954, pp. 1110–1114.

PAUNCZ, ARPAD, "Theory of the 'Total Push' Program in Psychiatry," *American Journal of Psychotherapy*, vol. 8, January, 1954, pp. 11–20.

PETERS, H. N., and R. L. JENKINS, "Improvement of Chronic Schizo-phrenic Patients with Guided Problem-Solving, Motivated by Hunger," *Psychiatric Quarterly* SUPPLEMENT, vol. 28, 1954, pp. 84–101.

RIOCH, D. McK., and A. H. STANTON, "Milieu Therapy," *Psychiatry*, vol. 16, February, 1953, pp. 65–72.

ROLAND, P. E., "An Exploratory Training Technique for the Re-education of Catatonics," *American Journal of Psychiatry*, vol. 105, November, 1948, pp. 353–356.

ROSE, D. M., and M. C. BUTLER, "Socio-psychiatric Backgrounds and Treatment of Some Psychotic Women," *Psychiatric Quarterly* SUPPLEMENT, vol. 28, 1954, pp. 279–296.

ROWELL, JOHN T., "An Approach to the Treatment of Massive Mental Hospital Population," *Mental Hygiene*, vol. 39, October, 1955, pp. 622–630.

SCHLOSSER, J. R., R. E. BUEHLER, and R. SANDERS, "Pilot Study for the Treatment of Chronic Patients," *VA Information Bulletin*, Dept. of Medicine and Surgery, Psychiatry and Neurology Service, October, 1954, pp. 10–68.

SCHNADT, FREDERICK, "A Plan for Rehabilitating Improved Psychotic Patients," *American Journal of Psychiatry*, vol. 110, October, 1953, pp. 253–260.

SCHWARTZ, M. S., and E. L. SHOCKLEY, *The Nurse and the Mental Patient: A Study in Interpersonal Relations*. Russell Sage Foundation, New York, 1956.

SEMRAD, E. V., and WILLIAM CORWIN, "Total Push Treatment of Chronic Schizophrenia at the Metropolitan State Hospital: Pre-liminary Report," *Archives of Neurology and Psychiatry*, vol. 44, July, 1940, pp. 232–233.

SEWALL, L. G., J. GILLIN, and F. M. LeBAR, "Through the Patient's Eyes," *Mental Hygiene*, vol. 39, April, 1955, pp. 284–292.

SIMMEL, E., "Psychoanalytic Treatment in a Sanatorium," *International Journal of Psychoanalysis*, vol. 10, January, 1929, pp. 70–89.

SIMON, H., *Aktivere Krankenbehandlung in der Irrenanstalt* (More Active Treatment in Mental Institutions). De Gruyter and Co., Berlin-Leipzig, 1929.

SINDLINGER, ELIZABETH, and MILDRED FARIS, "Nurse and Social Worker Collaborate in a Milieu Program," *Nursing Outlook*, vol. 3, May, 1955, pp. 296–298.

Sines, J. O., R. J. Lucero, and G. R. Kamman, "A State Hospital 'Total Push' Program for Regressed Schizophrenics," *Journal of Clinical Psychology*, vol. 8, 1952, pp. 189–193.

Stainbrook, Edward, "The Hospital as a Therapeutic Community," *Neuropsychiatry*, vol. 3, 1955, pp. 69–87.

Stanton, A. H., and M. S. Schwartz, "The Management of a Type of Institutional Participation in Mental Illness," *Psychiatry*, vol. 12, February, 1949, pp. 13–26.

Stanton, A. H., and M. S. Schwartz, *The Mental Hospital: A Study of Institutional Participation in Psychiatric Illness and Treatment*. Basic Books, New York, 1954.

Tarnower, William, "A Treatment Program for Open-Ward Neuropsychiatric Patients," *Bulletin of Menninger Clinic*, vol. 17, September, 1953, pp. 189–195.

Wayne, George J., "Work as Therapy, with Special Reference to the Elderly," *Mental Hygiene*, vol. 39, January, 1955, pp. 79–88.

Willner, G. P., "Preliminary Report of the Introduction of Group Psychotherapy on a Chronic Ward in a Mental Hospital," *Psychiatric Quarterly* Supplement, vol. 26, 1952, pp. 86–92.

Wittkower, E. D., and J. D. La Tendresse, "Rehabilitation of Chronic Schizophrenics by a New Method of Occupational Therapy," *British Journal of Medical Psychology*, vol. 28, 1955, pp. 42–47.

Yoder, O. R., "A Socialization Program in the Treatment of Dementia Praecox," *Occupational Therapy and Rehabilitation*, vol. 17, April, 1938, pp. 107–115.

Index

Index

211